Contents

*

Preface

*

JOHN L. BELL

CONVENER, EDITORIAL COMMITTEE

The song of the Church has always provided common ground. Baptists, Roman Catholics, Presbyterians, Congregationalists, Methodists, Anglicans and all other major Christian traditions have unfailingly borrowed from each other when music for worship was required.

What has been less common is the will to work co-operatively in providing a book as ecumenical in its preparation as in its contents. This book is the fruit of such rare co-operation.

Representatives from the major Christian traditions in Scotland met over two years to select words and music which reflect both the richness within their diverse traditions and the shared desire for songs which speak to and for God's worshipping people today.

The working party considered over 4000 texts and tunes, many of them suggested by members of the co-operating churches, some found in recent publications, others submitted by writers and composers. These were all considered with the authorship remaining anonymous, and subject to three restrictions:

1. choruses and praise songs, already widely known and memorised, were, in the main, excluded in order that newer material might be published;

2. historical hymns were avoided, as their place is more properly in denominational hymnaries than in supplementary collections of contemporary songs;

3. participative songs were preferred to performance pieces requiring skilled vocalists or instrumentalists. Worship is not a consumer activity in which we listen to our favourite song, but an engagement of all the people of God together in the presence of their Maker.

Of course, exceptions have been made, but the main intention has been to provide material which is new, accessible and grounded in biblical truth rather than individualistic experience.

Because the book has been produced in Scotland, there has also been a bias towards Scottish writers and tunesmiths. The Scottish churches do not have a proud history of encouraging the creative arts, but recent experience suggests a change in attitude. Over a third of the texts and tunes in *Common Ground* are Scottish in origin, representing over 26 different authors and 15 different composers. It is to be hoped, among other things, that the book will encourage others to use their writing skills in the service of the Church.

However, this supply of indigenous talent has not limited the inclusion of material from elsewhere. Uniquely among publications of this kind, *Common Ground* takes over 20 per cent of its material from nations in the southern hemisphere. It also introduces to British Christians a number of contemporary writers published in the USA who bear witness to the resurgence of interest in congregational song in the Roman Catholic Church in the wake of Vatican II.

With the diversity of sources of text and tune comes the possibility of discovering new ways to sing, accompany, and incorporate people in musical leadership. Where 50 years ago almost every child leaving Scottish schools understood *sol fa* notation and could be drafted into a choir, now young people leave school with different musical skills. The challenge to contemporary church musicians is to find ways of allowing this new talent to be put to the service of the Church as adventurously as the ability of previous generations.

The editorial group responsible for *Common Ground* sincerely hopes and desires that the spirit of openness, sensitivity and encouragement which pervaded our work may also be real among those who use the book.

And may God who has inspired the authors, composers, arrangers, selectors and editors enable in the singing of our churches a new passion for the praise of our Maker, a new fervour in commitment to God's world, and a new desire to celebrate unity within our diversity in response to the Lord's earnest prayer that 'they may be one'.

LENT 1998

'For all the Churches'

*

CHARLES ROBERTSON

SECRETARY, EDITORIAL COMMITTEE
AND CONVENER, PANEL ON WORSHIP

When the General Assembly of the Church of Scotland entrusted the Panel on Worship with the task of producing a successor to *Songs of God's People*, the suggestion that the new Supplement should be an ecumenical endeavour was gladly adopted.

The experience of working together to produce the book was stimulating and engaging, and thanks are due to those who so willingly and happily gave themselves to the enterprise. They were Mgr Gerry Fitzpatrick, Fr Paul Moore, Bro. Stephen Smythe and Mr Vincent Wallace (Roman Catholic Church); Mrs Sally-Anne Porter (Scottish Episcopal Church); The Revd Tom Wilkinson (Synod of the Methodist Church in Scotland); Mr George Barr (United Reformed Church); The Revd John Young (Scottish Congregational Church); Major David Gauton (Salvation Army); Messrs Ian McCrorie, Robert Tait, The Very Revd Gilleasbuig Macmillan, The Revd Dr Ian Bradley, The Revds John L. Bell, Charles Robertson, Maxwell Craig, Marion Dodd, Leith Fisher, Douglas Galbraith, Colin Renwick, and Alexander Young (Church of Scotland).

The editorial committee is especially indebted, as indeed are all the Churches, to John Bell and Douglas Galbraith who were responsible for editing the material and preparing the book for publication. The committee is also grateful for the patience and encouragement of our publishers, Saint Andrew Press, particularly the Publishing Manager, Lesley Taylor, and the Sales and Production Manager, Derek Auld, as well as Neil Gowans who set the music and Ann Gowans who worked on the text of the music edition.

Common Ground is now offered in the confidence that its use will enrich the worship of the people of God. The sense of privilege I feel in being associated with its publication is accompanied by the prayer that it will be much used and be a blessing to all the Churches.

LENT 1998

1

A Touching Place

1. Christ's is the world in which we move;
    Christ's are the folk we're summoned to love;
    Christ's is the voice that calls us to care,
    and Christ is the one who meets us here.
    To the lost Christ shows his face,
    to the unloved he gives his embrace,
    to those who cry in pain or disgrace,
    Christ makes, with his friends, a touching
        place.

2. Feel for the people we most avoid –
    strange or bereaved or never employed.
    Feel for the women and feel for the men
    who fear that their living is all in vain.

3. Feel for the parents who've lost their child,
    feel for the women whom men have defiled,
    feel for the baby for whom there's no breast,
    and feel for the weary who find no rest.

4. Feel for the lives by life confused,
    riddled with doubt, in loving abused;
    feel for the lonely heart, conscious of sin,
    which longs to be pure but fears to begin.

John L. Bell and Graham Maule

2

Abundant Life

1. We cannot own the sunlit sky,
    the moon, the wild flowers growing,
    for we are part of all that is

within life's river flowing.
With open hands receive and share
the gifts of God's creation,
that all may have abundant life
in every earthly nation.

2. When bodies shiver in the night
    and weary, wait for morning,
    when children have no bread but tears,
    and war-horns sound their warning,
    God calls humanity to wake,
    to join in common labour,
    that all may have abundant life
    in oneness with their neighbour.

3. God calls humanity to join
    as partners in creating
    a future free from want or fear,
    life's goodness celebrating.
    That new world beckons from afar,
    invites our shared endeavour,
    that all may have abundant life
    and peace endure for ever.

Ruth Duck

3

Agnus Dei

Lamb of God, you take away the sins of the world,
    have mercy on us.
Lamb of God, you take away the sins of the world,
    have mercy on us.
Lamb of God, you take away the sins of the world,
    grant us peace.

Liturgical text

4

All are welcome

1. Let us build a house where love can dwell
   and all can safely live,
   a place where saints and children tell
   how hearts learn to forgive.
   Built of hopes and dreams and visions,
   rock of faith and vault of grace;
   here the love of Christ shall end divisions:
   All are welcome, all are welcome,
   all are welcome in this place.

2. Let us build a house where prophets speak,
   and words are strong and true,
   where all God's children dare to seek
   to dream God's reign anew.
   Here the cross shall stand as witness
   and as symbol of God's grace;
   here as one we claim the faith of Jesus:

3. Let us build a house where love is found
   in water, wine and wheat:
   a banquet hall on holy ground
   where peace and justice meet.
   Here the love of God, through Jesus,
   is revealed in time and space;
   as we share in Christ the feast that frees us:

4. Let us build a house where hands will reach
   beyond the wood and stone
   to heal and strengthen, serve and teach,
   and live the Word they've known.
   Here the outcast and the stranger
   bear the image of God's face;
   let us bring an end to fear and danger:

5. Let us build a house where all are named,
   their songs and visions heard
   and loved and treasured, taught and claimed
   as words within the Word.
   Built of tears and cries and laughter,
   prayers of faith and songs of grace,
   let this house proclaim from floor to rafter:

   Marty Haugen

5

Alleluia.

South African setting

6

1. Amazing grace – how sweet the sound –
   that saved a wretch like me!
   I once was lost, but now am found,
   was blind, but now I see.

2. 'Twas grace that taught my heart to fear,
   and grace my fears relieved;
   how precious did that grace appear
   the hour I first believed!

3. Through many dangers, toils and snares
   I have already come;
   'tis grace has brought me safe thus far,
   and grace will lead me home.

4. The Lord has promised good to me,
   his word my hope secures;
   he will my shield and portion be
   as long as life endures.

   John Newton

7

Amen siakudumisa.
Amen siakudumisa.
Amen bawo, amen bawo,
amen siakudumisa.

(Amen. Praise the name of the Lord.)

South African traditional

8

1. As a fire is meant for burning
   with a bright and warming flame,
   so the church is meant for mission,
   giving glory to God's name.
   Not to preach our creeds or customs,
   but to build a bridge of care,
   we join hands across the nations,
   finding neighbours everywhere.

2. We are learners; we are teachers;
   we are pilgrims on the way.
   We are seekers; we are givers;
   we are vessels made of clay.
   By our gentle, loving actions,
   we would show that Christ is light.
   In a humble, listening Spirit,
   we would live to God's delight.

3. As a green bud in the springtime
   is a sign of life renewed,
   so may we be signs of oneness
   'mid earth's peoples, many hued.

As a rainbow lights the heavens
when a storm is past and gone,
may our lives reflect the radiance
of God's new and glorious dawn.

Ruth Duck

9

1. As many stones, their edges rough, unhewn,
   may by their awkward shape lend others
     strength,
   build up your church, Lord Christ, so that at
     length
   the various shapes harmoniously attune,
   and we are raised, a Temple to your fame,
   whose worship shall give glory to your name.

2. For not to the likeminded did you look
   to make a Church constructed of one kind,
   but quite unlikely folk in heart and mind
   to weld in one community you took
   and raised them up, a Temple to your fame,
   whose worship shall give glory to your name.

3. Then grant us, Lord, in others to delight,
   not those we like, but those now called by you;
   with all our awkward edges strength imbue
   that we may give folk shelter, warmth and light,
   that we be raised a Temple to your fame
   whose worship will give glory to your name.

Ian M. Fraser

10

As the deer longs for running streams,
so I long, so I long, so I long for you.

1. Athirst my soul for you, the God who is my life!
   When shall I see, when shall I see,
   see the face of God?

2. Echoes meet as deep is calling unto deep,
   over my head, all your mighty waters,
   sweeping over me.

3. Continually the foe delights in taunting me:
   'Where is God, where is your God?'
   Where, O where are you?

4. Defend me God, send forth your light and your
       truth,
   they will lead me to your holy mountain,
   to your dwelling place.

5. Then I shall go unto the altar of my God,
   praising you, O my joy and gladness:
   I shall praise your name.

Psalm 42-3(41-2), paraphrased by Bob Hurd

11

1. As two we love are wed this day
   and we stand witness to their vow,
   we ask the Holy Trinity
   to sanctify their pledges now.
       Praise, praise the Maker, Spirit, Son,
       blessing this marriage now begun.

2. Parents and families they leave,
   their own new family to make;
   and, sharing what their pasts have taught,
   they shape it for the future's sake.

3. This is as God meant it to be,
   that man and woman should be one
   and live in love and love through life,
   as Christ on earth has taught and done.

4. Then, bless the bridegroom, bless the bride,
   the dreams they dream, the hopes they share;
   and thank the Lord whose love inspires
   the joy their lips and ours declare.

John L. Bell and Graham Maule

12

1. Be still,
     for the presence of the Lord,
       the Holy One, is here;
     come bow before him now
     with reverence and fear:
     in him no sin is found –
     we stand on holy ground.
   Be still,
     for the presence of the Lord,
       the Holy One, is here.

2. Be still,
     for the glory of the Lord
       is shining all around;
     he burns with holy fire,
     with splendour he is crowned:
     how awesome is the sight –
     our radiant King of light!

Be still,
for the glory of the Lord
   is shining all around.

3.   Be still,
for the power of the Lord
   is moving in this place:
he comes to cleanse and heal,
to minister his grace –
no work too hard for him.
In faith receive from him.
Be still,
for the power of the Lord
   is moving in this place.

David J. Evans

13

Behold the lamb of God,
behold the lamb of God
who takes away the sin,
the sin of the world.

John 1: 29

14

Bless the Lord, my soul,
and bless God's holy name.
Bless the Lord, my soul,
who leads me into life.

from Psalm 103(102),
Taizé Community

15

a. The Song of Zechariah
(*Benedictus*)

1. Blest be the Lord, the God of Israel,
   who brings the dawn and darkest night dispels,
   who raises up a mighty saviour from the earth,
   of David's line, a son of royal birth.

2. The prophets tell a story just begun
   of vanquished foe and glorious victory won,
   of promise made to all who keep the law
      as guide:
   God's faithful love and mercy will abide.

MEN:
3. This is the oath once sworn to Abraham:
   all shall be free to dwell upon the land,
   free now to praise, unharmed by the
      oppressor's rod,
   holy and righteous in the sight of God.

WOMEN:
4. And you, my child, this day you shall be called
   the promised one, the prophet of our God,
   for you will go before the Lord to clear the way,
   and shepherd all into the light of day.

5. The tender love God promised from our birth
   is soon to dawn upon this shadowed earth,
   to shine on those whose sorrows seem to
      never cease,
   to guide our feet into the path of peace.

Luke 1: 68-79,
paraphrased by Owen Alstott

b. The Song of Mary
(*Magnificat*)

1. My soul proclaims the greatness of the Lord.
   My spirit sings to God, my saving God,
   who on this day above all others favoured me
   and raised me up, a light for all to see.

2. Through me great deeds will God make
      manifest,
   and all the earth will come to call me blest.
   Unbounded love and mercy sure will I
      proclaim
   for all who know and praise God's holy name.

3. God's mighty arm, protector of the just,
   will guard the weak and raise them from the
      dust.
   But mighty kings will swiftly fall from thrones
      corrupt,
   the strong brought low, the lowly lifted up.

4. Soon will the poor and hungry of the earth
   be richly blest, be given greater worth,
   and Israel, as once foretold to Abraham,
   will live in peace throughout the promised
      land.

5. All glory be to God, Creator blest,
   to Jesus Christ, God's love made manifest,
   and to the Holy Spirit, gentle Comforter,
   all glory be, both now and evermore.

Luke 1: 46-55,
paraphrased by Owen Alstott

16

1. Brother, Sister, let me serve you,
   let me be as Christ to you;
   pray that I may have the grace to
   let you be my servant too.

2. We are pilgrims on a journey,
   and companions on the road;
   we are here to help each other
   walk the mile and bear the load.

3. I will hold the Christ-light for you
   in the night-time of your fear;
   I will hold my hand out to you,
   speak the peace you long to hear.

4. I will weep when you are weeping;
   when you laugh I'll laugh with you;
   I will share your joy and sorrow
   till we've seen this journey through.

5. When we sing to God in heaven
   we shall find such harmony,
   born of all we've known together
   of Christ's love and agony.

6. Brother, Sister, let me serve you,
   let me be as Christ to you;
   pray that I may have the grace to
   let you be my servant too.

Richard Gillard

17

1. Bread is blessed and broken,
   wine is blessed and poured:
   take this and remember
   Christ the Lord.

2. Share the food of heaven
   earth can not afford.
   Here is grace in essence –
   Christ the Lord.

3. Know yourself forgiven,
   find yourself restored,
   meet a friend for ever –
   Christ the Lord.

4. God has kept his promise
   sealed by sign and word:
   here, for those who want him –
   Christ the Lord.

John L. Bell and Graham Maule

18

Come all you people,
come and praise your Maker; (x 3)
come now and worship the Lord.

Uyai mose, tinamate Mwari; (x 3)
Uyai mose zvino.

from Psalm 100(99),
Alexander Gondo

19

Celtic Alleluia

REFRAIN:
> *Alleluia, alleluia!*
> *Alleluia, alleluia!*

1. The Word of the Lord lasts for ever.
    What is the Word that is living?
    It is brought to us through his Son Jesus Christ.

2. God brings the world to himself
    now through his Christ reconciling;
    he has trusted us with the news of redeeming
    love.

3. The Word of the Lord is alive,
    the Word of God is active –
    it can judge our thoughts, bring us closer to the
    Father.

4. Father of all you are blessed,
    creator of earth and heaven,
    for the mysteries of the kingdom shown to
    children.

5. 'I call you friends,' says the Lord,
    'you who are my disciples.
    I make known to you all I've learned from my
    Father.'

6. 'The sheep of my flock,' says the Lord,
    'hearing my voice, they will listen;
    they will follow me, for I know them, they are
    mine.'

7. 'Even if you have to die,
   close to my Word keep faithful;
   for your faithfulness I will give you the crown
      of life.'

8. Stay awake, pray at all times,
   praying that you may be strengthened,
   that with confidence you can meet the Son of
      Man.

Fintan O'Carroll and Christopher Walker

20

1. Clap your hands all you nations,
      Amen. Hallelujah!
   shout for joy all you people;
      Amen. Hallelujah!
   Holy is the most high;
      Amen. Hallelujah!
   mighty over the earth.
      Amen. Hallelujah!

2. God subdues every nation,
   God is king of all creatures;
   God has given this land
   to the people he loves.

3. To the shouting in triumph,
   to the blasting of trumpets,
   God has gone up,
   God ascends over all.

4. Praise the Lord with your singing,
   sing God psalms for ever.
   God is monarch of all,
   sovereign over the earth.

5. Those on earth who are mighty
   still belong to our Maker,
   God exalted on high,
   God forever our Lord.

   Psalm 47(46),
   paraphrased by John L. Bell

21

Christ be our Light

1. Longing for light, we wait in darkness.
   Longing for truth, we turn to you.
   Make us your own, your holy people,
   light for the world to see.
     Christ, be our light!
     Shine in our hearts.
     Shine through the darkness.
     Christ, be our light!
     Shine in your church
     gathered today.

2. Longing for peace, our world is troubled.
   Longing for hope, many despair.
   Your word alone has power to save us.
   Make us your living voice.

3. Longing for food, many are hungry.
   Longing for water, many still thirst.
   Make us your bread, broken for others,
   shared until all are fed.

4. Longing for shelter, many are homeless,
   Longing for warmth, many are cold.
   Make us your building, sheltering others,
   walls made of living stone.

5. Many the gifts, many the people,
   many the hearts that yearn to belong.
   Let us be servants to one another,
   making your kingdom come.

   Bernadette Farrell

22

1. Come, let us seek our God's protection,
   Yesu sets us free to love and serve.
   Yesu sets us free.

2. For sin and self and fear enslave us …

3. When eyes are tired from too much weeping …

4. God knows our suffering, sees our trouble …

5. God is our refuge and defender …

6. How wonderful God's constant love is …

7. Our God unites us as one people …

8. Let's dance and sing to God our Saviour …

9. And shout for joy with all God's children …

10. Haleluya, yes, Haleluya …

    Tom Colvin

23

Come and gather round

1. Says Jesus, 'Come and gather round.
    I want to teach my friends
    some truths about the love I bring,
    the love that never ends.
    Look to the child, here in your midst,
    who has so much and more to say
    of what it means to follow me,
    to come and walk my way.'

2. Christ speaks to us who, growing old,
    get burdened down with care;
    while caution reigns, we seldom see
    God's presence everywhere.
    He points to gifts that children bring –
    the will to risk, the trust to dare,
    through which, no matter where we are,
    we'll find God always there.

3. When was it that we first forgot
    that questions helped us grow,
    or lost the openness to ask
    and learn what we don't know?
    Christ points to gifts that children bring,
    the searching heart and lively mind
    which let God's kingdom grow in those
    who seek until they find.

4. Lord Jesus, we have gathered round
    to hear you teach your friends
    the truths about the love you bring,
    that love which never ends.
    We look to children in our midst
    for they have much and more to say
    and join with them to follow you,
    to live and walk your way.

Leith Fisher

24

1. Come, my Way, my Truth, my Life:
   such a way as gives us breath;
   such a truth as ends all strife;
   such a life as conquers death.

2. Come, my Light, my Feast, my Strength:
   such a light as shows a feast;
   such a feast as mends in length;
   such a strength as makes a guest.

3. Come, my Joy, my Love, my Heart:
   such a joy as none can move;
   such a love as none can part;
   such a heart as joys in love.

George Herbert

25

1. Come now, O Prince of peace,
   make us one body,
   come, O Lord Jesus,
   reconcile your people.

2. Come now, O God of love,
   make us one body,
   come, O Lord Jesus,
   reconcile your people.

3. Come now and set us free,
   O God, our Saviour,
   come, O Lord Jesus,
   reconcile all nations.

4. Come, Hope of unity,
   make us one body,
   come, O Lord Jesus,
   reconcile all nations.

Geonyong Lee,
revised by Marion Pope

26

Come to me and I shall give you rest.

1. From the depths I call to you.
   Listen, Lord, and hear my pleading.

2. Love and mercy flow from you,
   Lord of life and kind redeemer.

3. In the dark I hope for you,
   you are light of new day dawning.

4. Weak and frail we come to you,
   God of love and new beginning.

Psalm 130(129),
paraphrased by Noel Donnelly

27

1. Comes Mary to the grave:
   no singing bird has spoken,
   nor has the world awoken,
   and in her grief all love lies lost
       and broken.

2. Says Jesus at her side,
   no longer Jesus dying,

'Why, Mary, are you crying?'
She turns, with joy, 'My Lord! My love!'
    replying.

3.   With Mary on this day
    we join our voices praising
    the God of Jesus' raising,
    and sing the triumph of his love
        amazing.

Michael Perry

28

1.   Comfort, comfort now my people;
    speak of peace – so says your God.
    Comfort those who sit in darkness,
    burdened by a heavy load.
    To Jerusalem proclaim:
    God shall take away your shame.
    Now get ready to recover;
    guilt and suffering are over.

2.   Hear the herald's proclamation
    in the desert far and near,
    calling all to true repentance,
    telling that the Lord is near.
    Oh, that warning cry obey!
    For your God prepare a way.
    Let the valleys rise to greet him
    and the hills bow down to meet him.

3.   Straighten out what has been crooked;
    make the roughest places plain.
    Let your hearts be true and humble,
    live as fits God's holy reign.
    Soon the glory of the Lord

shall on earth be shed abroad.
Human flesh shall surely see it;
God is ready to decree it.

Isaiah 40: 1-5,
paraphrased by Johannes Olearius,
translated by Catherine Winkworth,
amended by John L. Bell

29

Dignity and Grace

1. When I receive the peace of Christ
    my loneliness shall end;
    and I must reach a hand and take
    my brother as a friend,
    my brother as a friend indeed
    who has an honoured place
    where he may stand before the Lord
    in dignity and grace.

2. When I receive the peace of Christ
    my loneliness shall end;
    and I must reach a hand and take
    my sister as a friend,
    my sister as a friend indeed
    who has an honoured place
    where she may stand before the Lord
    in dignity and grace.

3. When I receive the peace of Christ
    my loneliness shall end;
    and I must reach a hand and take
    my own self as a friend,
    my own self as a friend indeed
    who has an honoured place
    where I may stand before the Lord
    in dignity and grace.

4. When I receive the peace of Christ
   my loneliness shall end;
   and I must reach a hand and take
   Christ Jesus as a friend,
   Christ Jesus as a friend indeed
   who has an honoured place
   where now he stands amongst us all
   in dignity and grace.

Michael Mair

30

Eastertide
Gospel Acclamation

REFRAIN:
   Alleluia, alleluia,
   Jesus, risen Lord of life!
   Alleluia, alleluia, alleluia!

1. Word of the Father: *Jesus Christ!*
   Hope of the world: *Jesus Christ!*
   Broken and buried: *Jesus Christ!*
   Risen to life: *Jesus Christ!*

2. Light of the nations: *Jesus Christ!*
   Way, Truth and Life: *Jesus Christ!*
   Bearing our sorrow: *Jesus Christ!*
   With us through time: *Jesus Christ!*

3. Living among us: *Jesus Christ!*
   Word in our flesh: *Jesus Christ!*
   Servant of others: *Jesus Christ!*
   Friend of the poor: *Jesus Christ!*

Bernadette Farrell

31

Eat this bread, drink this cup,
come to me and never be hungry.
Eat this bread, drink this cup,
trust in me and you will not thirst.

from John 6, Taizé Community

32

Enemy of Apathy

1. She sits like a bird, brooding on the waters,
    hovering on the chaos of the world's first day;
    she sighs and she sings, mothering creation,
    waiting to give birth to all the Word will say.

2. She wings over earth, resting where she wishes,
    lighting close at hand or soaring through the
        skies;
    she nests in the womb, welcoming each wonder,
    nourishing potential hidden to our eyes.

3. She dances in fire, startling her spectators,
    waking tongues of ecstasy where dumbness
        reigned;
    she weans and inspires all whose hearts are
        open,
    nor can she be captured, silenced or restrained.

4. For she is the Spirit, one with God in essence,
    gifted by the Saviour in eternal love;
    she is the key opening the scriptures,
    enemy of apathy and heavenly dove.

John L. Bell and Graham Maule

33
Final Commendation

ANTIPHON:
Receive her *soul, receive* her *soul*
and present her *to God, the Most High.*
Receive her *soul, receive* her *soul*
and present her *to God, the Most High.*

1. Saints of God, come to *her* aid!
   Hasten to meet *her,* angels of the Lord.

2. May Christ, who called you, take you to himself,
   may angels lead you to Abraham's side.

3. Eternal rest give unto *her,* O Lord,
   and let perpetual light shine upon *her.*

from ICEL Order of Christian Funerals

34

1. For the fruits of all creation,
   thanks be to God;
   for these gifts to every nation,
   thanks be to God;
   for the ploughing, sowing, reaping,
   silent growth while we are sleeping,
   future needs in earth's safe-keeping,
   thanks be to God.

2. In the just reward of labour,
   God's will is done;
   in the help we give our neighbour,
   God's will is done;
   in our world-wide task of caring
   for the hungry and despairing,

in the harvests we are sharing,
God's will is done.

3. For the harvests of the Spirit,
    thanks be to God;
    for the good we all inherit,
    thanks be to God;
    for the wonders that astound us,
    for the truths that still confound us,
    most of all, that love has found us,
    thanks be to God.

Fred Pratt Green

35

1. For your generous providing
    which sustains us all our days,
    for your Spirit here residing,
    we proclaim our heartfelt praise.
    Through the depths of joy and sorrow,
    though the road be smooth or rough,
    fearless, we can face tomorrow
    for your grace will be enough.

2. Hush our world's seductive voices
    tempting us to stand alone;
    save us, then, from siren noises
    calling us to trust our own.
    For those snared by earthly treasure,
    lured by false security,
    Jesus, true and only measure,
    spring the trap to set folk free.

3. Round your table, through your giving,
    show us how to live and pray
    till your kingdom's way of living
    is the bread we share each day:

bread for us and for our neighbour,
bread for body, mind, and soul,
bread of heaven and human labour –
broken bread that makes us whole.

Leith Fisher

36

1. Forgiveness is your gift,
   both cleansing and renewing,
   to catch us when we drift,
   our base desires pursuing;
   and hug us back to life
   and bring us to a feast
   where all will celebrate
   the life your love released.

2. Your grace goes out to meet
   the sinful and the doubting,
   your arms and dancing feet
   speak louder than all shouting:
   O God, how great your love
   which takes us empty in,
   and, with our worth unproved,
   lets better life begin.

Ian M. Fraser

37

1. Forty days and forty nights in Judah's desert
   Jesus stayed;
   all alone he fought temptation, all alone he
   fasted, prayed.
   When the heat of passion rules me, when I feel
   alone, betrayed,

Lord, you meet me in the desert, strong in
    faith and unafraid.

2.   In the garden, his disciples slept the darkest
    hours away,
    but our Lord did not condemn them when they
    would not watch or pray.
    Make me constant in your service, keeping
    watch both night and day.
    Give me grace that I may never such a love as
    yours betray.

3.   When the rooster crowed at daybreak, Peter's
    fear and panic grew.
    He denied three times the charge that Jesus
    was a man he knew.
    When my love for you is challenged, when the
    faithful ones are few,
    give me courage and conviction to proclaim my
    Lord anew.

4.   Soldiers came, the Galilean was arrested, bound
    and tried,
    and upon a wooden cross the Son of God was
    crucified.
    In the darkest hour of torture, Jesus raised his
    head and cried,
    'Why hast thou forsaken me?' and, faithful to
    the end, he died.

5.   With a sword they pierced his side – himself,
    they jeered, he could not save;
    Joseph then prepared the body with sweet
    spices for the grave.
    This the precious, broken body which for me
    my Saviour gave;
    such a love as his I long for, such a faith as his
    I crave.

Jean Holloway

38
Gather us in

1. Here in this place new light is streaming,
   now is the darkness vanished away,
   see in this space our fears and our dreamings,
   brought here to you in the light of this day.
   Gather us in – the lost and forsaken,
   gather us in – the blind and the lame;
   call to us now, and we shall awaken,
   we shall arise at the sound of our name.

2. We are the young – our lives are a mystery,
   we are the old who yearn for your face,
   we have been sung throughout all of history,
   called to be light to the whole human race.
   Gather us in – the rich and the haughty,
   gather us in – the proud and the strong;
   give us a heart so meek and so lowly,
   give us the courage to enter the song.

3. Here we will take the wine and the water,
   here we will take the bread of new birth,
   here you shall call your sons and your
       daughters,
   call us anew to be salt for the earth.
   Give us to drink the wine of compassion,
   give us to eat the bread that is you;
   nourish us well, and teach us to fashion
   lives that are holy and hearts that are true.

4. Not in the dark of buildings confining,
   not in some heaven, light years away,
   but here in this place the new light is shining,
   now is the Kingdom, now is the day.
   Gather us in and hold us for ever,

gather us in and make us your own;
gather us in – all peoples together,
fire of love in our flesh and our bone.

Marty Haugen

39

1. Glory to God above!
   Heavens declare his love;
   praise him, you angels,
   praise him all you high and heavenly host.
   Worship him, sun and moon;
   stars, complement their tune;
   grounded in God's good purpose,
   let his grace become your boast.
      O sing hallelujah
      and praise God for ever more.

2. Glory to God below
   let depths of ocean show;
   lightning and hail, snow,
   wind and cloud perform at his command!
   Let every mountain range,
   forest and grove and grange,
   creatures of earth and air and sea
   praise God in every land.

3. 'Glory to God!' now sing
   commoner, queen and king;
   women and men of
   every age unite to praise the Lord.
   Worship God's holy name
   and let your lives proclaim
   God's saving power extends to those
   who love and serve his word.
      O sing hallelujah
      and praise God for ever, ever more.

Psalm 148, paraphrased by John L. Bell

40

1. God give us life
   when all around spells death
   and some have died;
   and few are clear that hope is near
   or fate can be defied.

2. God give us love
   in heart and hand
   to hold the hurting one,
   to free the anger, meet the need
   and wait till waiting's done.

3. God give us skill,
   insight and will
   to find, where none are sure,
   new threads to mend the web of life,
   new means to heal and cure.

4. God give us faith,
   should all else fail
   and death unsheath its sting.
   O help us hear, through pain and fear,
   the songs that angels sing.

5. Then, in the end,
   make death a friend,
   and give us strength to stand
   and walk to where no eye can stare,
   but Christ can clasp our hand.

John L. Bell and Graham Maule

41

1. God the Father of Creation,
   source of life and energy,

your creative love so shapes us
that we share your liberty.
Teach us how to use this freedom
loving children all to be.

2. Jesus Christ our Lord and brother,
   in your cross we see the way
   to be servants for each other,
   caring, suffering every day.
   Teach us patience and obedience
   never from your path to stray.

3. Holy Spirit, love that binds us
   to the Father and the Son,
   giver of the joy that fills us,
   yours the peace that makes us one,
   teach our hearts to be more open
   so to pray, 'God's will be done'.

4. Members of our Saviour's body,
   here on earth his life to be,
   though we stand as different people,
   may we share the unity
   of the Father, Son and Spirit,
   perfect love in Trinity.

Iain D. Cunningham

42

God to enfold you,
Christ to uphold you,
Spirit to keep you in heaven's sight;
so may God grace you,
heal and embrace you,
lead you through darkness into the light.

John L. Bell

43

1. Great is thy faithfulness, O God my Father,
   there is no shadow of turning with thee;
   thou changest not, thy compassions they fail not,
   as thou hast been thou for ever wilt be.
     Great is thy faithfulness!
     Great is thy faithfulness!
     Morning by morning new mercies I see;
     all I have needed thy hand hath provided –
     great is thy faithfulness, Lord, unto me!

2. Summer and winter, and spring-time and
     harvest,
   sun, moon and stars in their courses above,
   join with all nature in manifold witness
   to thy great faithfulness, mercy and love.

3. Pardon for sin and a peace that endureth,
   thine own dear presence to cheer and to guide;
   strength for today and bright hope for
     tomorrow,
   blessings all mine, with ten thousand beside!

Thomas O. Chisholm

44

1. God's will for creation
   is Jesus' to do:
   new branches to wither,
   old trees to renew.
     Jesus! Jesus! Jesus!
     How can we help but praise him.

2. Each plant in its growing,
   each shape in the strand,
   are filled with God's blessing,
   are stirred by God's hand.

3. All life in the river,
   all fish in the sea,
   earth's numberless creatures
   God summoned to be.

4. Each bird in the morning,
   each star in the sky,
   proclaim the Lord's goodness
   which never can die.

* * *

1. Bu cho fus a dh'Iosa
   An crann crion ùradh,
   'S an crann ùr a chrionadh,
   Na'm b'e rùn a dhèanamh:
       Iosa! Iosa! Iosa!
       Iosa bu chòir a mholadh.

2. Ni bheil lus an làr,
   Nach bheil làn d'a thoradh;
   Ni bheil cruth an tràigh,
   Nach bheil làn d'a shonas:

3. Ni bheil creubh am fairge,
   Ni bheil dearg an abhainn,
   Ni bheil càil an fhailbhe,
   Nach bheil dearbh d'a mhaitheas:

4. Ni bheil ian air sgèith,
   Ni bheil reul an adhar,
   Ni bheil sian fo'n ghrèin,
   Nach tog sgeul d'a mhaitheas:

Gaelic traditional,
English version by Common Ground *editors*

45

1. Great God, your love has called us here
   as we, by love, for love were made.
   Your living likeness still we bear,
   though marred, dishonoured, disobeyed.
   > We come, with all our heart and mind
   > your call to hear, your love to find.

2. We come with self-inflicted pains
   of broken trust and chosen wrong,
   half-free, half-bound by inner chains,
   by social forces swept along,
   > by powers and systems close confined
   > yet seeking hope for humankind.

3. Great God, in Christ you call our name
   and then receive us as your own
   not through some merit, right or claim
   but by your gracious love alone.
   > We strain to glimpse your mercy seat
   > and find you kneeling at our feet.

4. Then take the towel, and break the bread,
   and humble us, and call us friends.
   Suffer and serve till all are fed,
   and show how grandly love intends
   > to work till all creation sings,
   > to fill all worlds, to crown all things.

5. Great God, in Christ you set us free
   your life to live, your joy to share.
   Give us your Spirit's liberty
   to turn from guilt and dull despair
   > and offer all that faith can do
   > while love is making all things new.

Brian Wren

46

1. Haven't you heard that Jesus is risen?
   Mary was there at crack of the dawn;
   weeping, she found him down in the garden:
   laughter is living and grieving is gone.
   > *Our hearts are glowing,*
   > *our eyes are showing*
   > *that Jesus lives.*

2. Haven't you heard that Jesus is risen?
   Cleopas told us. Evening drew on;
   walking and talking, travelling with them
   Jesus was present: now grieving is gone.

3. Haven't you heard that Jesus is risen?
   Peter was fishing. Out of the dawn
   Jesus called, 'Shoot your net to the starboard' –
   fishing is thriving and grieving is gone.

4. Haven't you heard that Jesus is risen?
   Haven't you heard that Jesus goes on?
   Haven't you heard that Jesus is with us?
   Laughter is living and grieving is gone.

Alison M. Robertson

47

1. Hear me, dear Lord, in this my time of sorrow.
   For even if I turn from you today
   I need to know your love is there tomorrow
   and new hope still can lighten up my way.

2. Forgive me, Lord, if in the tears of sadness
   my anger makes me take your name in vain,
   and life seems for a while to have no gladness
   and I refuse to let you share my pain.

3. Help me, my God, through all surrounding
    darkness,
    To hold by faith what often I have read,
    that even in death's unremitting starkness
    the Son of Man has risen from the dead.

4. So take this life that's left with its misgivings,
    from grief and pain create in me anew
    a faith that finds in you a way of living,
    a love that offers all it has to you.

Colin Ferguson

48

ENTRANCE SONG *or* SANCTUS:
    Holy, holy, holy,
    my heart, my heart adores you!
    My heart is glad to say the words:
    you are holy, Lord.

BENEDICTUS QUI VENIT:
    In God's name is coming
    the One whom we call blessed.
    Hosanna in the highest.
    Praise and thanks to God.

ACCLAMATION:
    You alone are holy,
    and you alone are Lord,
    and you alone are the most high
    Jesus Christ our Lord.

ORIGINAL:
    Santo, santo, santo,
    mi corazon te^adora!
    Mi corazon te sabe decir:
    santo^eres Señor.

from Argentina

49

1. Heaven shall not wait
   for the poor to lose their patience,
   the scorned to smile, the despised to find
      a friend:
   Jesus is Lord;
   he has championed the unwanted;
   in him injustice confronts its timely end.

2. Heaven shall not wait
   for the rich to share their fortunes,
   the proud to fall, the élite to tend the least:
   Jesus is Lord;
   he has shown the masters' privilege –
   to kneel and wash servants' feet before they
      feast.

3. Heaven shall not wait
   for the dawn of great ideas,
   thoughts of compassion divorced from cries
      of pain:
   Jesus is Lord;
   he has married word and action;
   his cross and company make his purpose plain.

4. Heaven shall not wait
   for triumphant Hallelujahs,
   when earth has passed and we reach another
      shore:
   Jesus is Lord
   in our present imperfection;
   his power and love are for now and then for
      ever more.

John L. Bell and Graham Maule

50
Here I am, Lord

1. I, the Lord of sea and sky,
    I have heard my people cry.
    All who dwell in dark and sin
    my hand will save.
    I, who made the stars of night,
    I will make their darkness bright.
    Who will bear my light to them?
    Whom shall I send?
    > *Here I am, Lord. Is it I, Lord?*
    > *I have heard you calling in the night.*
    > *I will go, Lord, if you lead me.*
    > *I will hold your people in my heart.*

2. I, the Lord of snow and rain,
    I have borne my people's pain.
    I have wept for love of them.
    They turn away.
    I will break their hearts of stone,
    give them hearts for love alone.
    I will speak my word to them.
    Whom shall I send?

3. I, the Lord of wind and flame,
    I will send the poor and lame.
    I will set a feast for them.
    My hand will save.
    Finest bread I will provide
    till their hearts be satisfied.
    I will give my life to them.
    Whom shall I send?

Daniel L. Schutte

51

How can I keep from singing

1. My life flows on in endless song
   above earth's lamentation.
   I catch the sweet, though far off, hymn
   that hails a new creation.
   > *No storm can shake my inmost calm*
   > *while to that Rock I'm clinging.*
   > *Since love is Lord of heaven and earth,*
   > *how can I keep from singing?*

2. Through all the tumult and the strife,
   I hear that music ringing.
   It finds an echo in my soul.
   How can I keep from singing?

3. What though my joys and comforts die?
   The Lord my Saviour liveth.
   What though the darkness round me close?
   Songs in the night he giveth.

4. The peace of Christ makes fresh my heart,
   a fountain ever springing.
   All things are mine since I am his!
   How can I keep from singing?

Robert Lowry and Doris Plenn

52

1. How good it is, what pleasure comes,
   when people live as one.
   When peace and justice light the way
   the will of God is done.

2. True friendship then like fragrant oil
   surrounds us with delight;
   and blessings shine like morning dew
   upon the mountain height.

3. How good it is when walls of fear
   come tumbling to the ground.
   When arms are changed to farming tools
   the fruits of life abound.

4. What quiet joy can bloom and grow
   when people work for peace,
   when hands and voices join as one
   that hate and war may cease.

Ruth Duck

53

How great Thou art

1. O Lord my God! when I in awesome wonder
   consider all the works thy hand hath made,
   I see the stars, I hear the mighty thunder,
   thy power throughout the universe displayed:
   > *Then sings my soul, my Saviour God, to
   > thee,*
   > *How great thou art, how great thou art!*
   > *Then sings my soul, my Saviour God, to
   > thee,*
   > *How great thou art, how great thou art!*

2. When through the woods and forest glades
   I wander
   and hear the birds sing sweetly in the trees;
   when I look down from lofty mountain
   grandeur,
   and hear the brook, and feel the gentle breeze:

3. And when I think that God his Son not sparing
   sent him to die – I scarce can take it in,
   that on the cross my burden gladly bearing,
   he bled and died to take away my sin:

4. When Christ shall come with shout of
      acclamation
   and take me home – what joy shall fill my
      heart!
   Then shall I bow in humble adoration
   and there proclaim, my God, how great thou art!

Russian hymn,
translated by Stuart K. Hine

54

1. How happy the pure who in the Lord's law
      walk.
   How happy those who keep his rules and seek
      him from the heart.
   They do no wrong, but walk in all his ways,
   for you command your precepts be carefully
      observed.
   If only my ways were steadfast in your law,
   I'd not be ashamed, beholding your commands.
   I'll praise you as I learn your righteous laws
   and I will keep your just decrees; do not
      abandon me.

2. How can young lives be pure but by your
      word?
   With all my heart I seek you; let me not go
      astray.
   Deep in my heart your promise I have stored
   to grieve you with no sin at all. Blessed Lord,
      teach me your way.

My lips tell of all the judgments of your mouth,
the way of your rules to me is great reward.
Your rules and paths I'll ponder and observe
and in your laws will I rejoice; I'll not forget
  your word.

3. Do good to me – I'll live and keep your word.
Make wide my eyes that I may see the wonders
  in your law.
A wanderer upon the earth am I!
Do not hide from me your commands my soul
  is longing for.
You spurn all the proud who stray from your
  commands.
Take from me their scorn for I have kept your
  law.
Though princes sit to plot against my life
your testimonies I'll recite; my counsellors are
  they all.

Psalm 119(118): 1-24,
translated by David Mitchell

55

1. I've waited long, said Simeon;
   today it has come true –
   the promise made so long ago
   is now fulfilled in you.
      The old has gone,
      the new has come.

2. The future is upon us now;
   the Law which kept us right
   is ancient history now as we
   emerge into the light …

3. The People of the Covenant
   in whom the promise grew
   will share their secret – now the hope
   of Gentile as of Jew …

4. Now custom and convention's hold
   will separate no more,
   nor culture keep the nations in
   perpetual state of war …

5. It's time to go, the old man said;
   a sign is given today,
   a light to comfort and reveal,
   to challenge and to free …

   Douglas Galbraith

56

1. I bow my knee in prayer
   before the Father who made me,
   before the Son who purchased me,
   before the Spirit who cleansed me,
       in friendship and love.

2. Lord, through your anointed,
   give us the fulness we long for:
   love and affection for our God,
   the smile and wisdom of our God,
       the grace of God.

3. So may we live on earth
   as saints and angels in heaven;
   each shade and light, each day and night,
   through every moment we draw our breath,
       God, give us your Spirit.

* * *

1. Ta mi lùbadh mo ghlùn
   An sùil an Athar a chruthaich mi,
   An sùil a' Mhic a cheannaich mi,
   An sùil an Spioraid a ghlanaich mi,
       Le gràdh agus rùn.

2. Dòirt a nuas orm à flathas,
   Tròcair shuairce do mhathais,
   Fhir tha'n uachdar na Cathair,
       Dèansa fathamas rinn.

3. Tabhair duinn a Shlàn'ear àigh,
   Eagal Dè, gaol Dè, agus gràdh,
   Is toil Dè dhèanamh air thalamh gach rè,
   Mar ni ainglich is naoimhich air néamh,
       Gach là agus oidhche thoir dhuinn do shéimh,
       Gach là agus oidhche thoir dhuinn do shéimh.

Gaelic traditional,
English version by Common Ground *editors*

57

1. I come with joy, a child of God,
       forgiven, loved and free,
   the life of Jesus to recall,
       in love laid down for me,
       in love laid down for me.

2. I come with Christians far and near
       to find, as all are fed,
   the new community of love
       in Christ's communion bread,
       in Christ's communion bread.

3. As Christ breaks bread, and bids us share,
  each proud division ends.
The love that made us, makes us one,
  and strangers now are friends,
  and strangers now are friends.

4. The Spirit of the risen Christ,
  unseen, but ever near,
is in such friendship better known,
  alive among us here,
  alive among us here.

5. Together met, together bound
  by all that God has done,
we'll go with joy, to give the world
  the love that makes us one,
  the love that makes us one.

Brian Wren

58

1. I know that my Redeemer lives,
  glory, hallelujah!
What comfort this sweet sentence gives,
  glory, hallelujah!
Shout on, pray on, we're gaining ground,
  glory, hallelujah!
The dead's alive and the lost is found,
  glory, hallelujah!

2. He lives to bless me with his love,
He lives to plead for me above,
He lives, my hungry soul to feed,
He lives, to help in time of need.

3. He lives, all glory to his name,
   He lives, my Saviour, still the same,
   What joy the bless'd assurance gives,
   I know that my Redeemer lives.

   Samuel Medley

59

1. I rejoiced when I heard them say:
   'Let us go to the house of God'.
   And now our feet are standing
   in your gates, O Jerusalem!
   Shalom, shalom,
   the peace of God be here.
   Shalom, shalom,
   God's justice be ever near.

2. Like a temple of unity
   is the city, Jerusalem.
   It is there all tribes will gather,
   all the tribes of the house of God.

3. It is faithful to Israel's law,
   there to praise the name of God.
   All the judgement seats of David
   were set down in Jerusalem.

4. For the peace of all nations, pray:
   for God's peace within your homes.
   May God's lasting peace surround us;
   may it dwell in Jerusalem.

5. For the love of my friends and kin
   I will bless you with signs of peace.

For the love of God's own people
I will labour and pray for you.

Psalm 122(121),
paraphrased by Bernadette Farrell

60

1. I waited patiently for God,
   for God to hear my prayer;
   and God bent down to where I sank
   and listened to me there.

2. God raised me from a miry pit,
   from mud and sinking sand,
   and set my feet upon a rock
   where I can firmly stand.

3. And on my lips a song was put,
   a new song to the Lord.
   Many will marvel, open-eyed,
   and put their trust in God.

4. Great wonders you have done, O Lord,
   all purposed for our good.
   Unable every one to name,
   I bow in gratitude.

Psalm 40(39),
paraphrased by John L. Bell

61

ANTIPHON:
I will walk in the presence of God.

1. I trusted when I felt afflicted,
   I walk in the sight of the Lord,
   and even in the face of death
   I will walk in the presence of God.

2. Your servant, Lord, is ever trusting.
   My bonds you have loosened with care.
   I offer thanks and sacrifice,
   I will walk in the presence of God.

3. My vows to God I keep with gladness,
   I dwell in the house of my Lord.
   My promises I will fulfil.
   I will walk in the presence of God.

from Psalm 116(115),
paraphrased by Noel Donnelly

62

If you believe and I believe
and we together pray,
the Holy Spirit shall come down
and set God's people free,
and set God's people free,
and set God's people free,
the Holy Spirit shall come down
and set God's people free.

Zimbabwean traditional

63

1. Inspired by love and anger,
      disturbed by need and pain,
   informed of God's own bias,
      we ask him once again:
   'How long must some folk suffer?
      How long can few folk mind?
   How long dare vain self interest
      turn prayer and pity blind?'

2. From those forever victims
      of heartless human greed,
   their cruel plight composes
      a litany of need:
   'Where are the fruits of justice?
      Where are the signs of peace?
   When is the day when prisoners
      and dreams find their release?'

*3. From those forever shackled
      to what their wealth can buy,
   the fear of lost advantage
      provokes the bitter cry,
   'Don't query our position!
      Don't criticise our wealth!
   Don't mention those exploited
      by politics and stealth!'

*4. To God, who through the prophets
      proclaimed a different age,
   we offer earth's indifference,
      its agony and rage:
   'When will the wronged be righted?
      When will the kingdom come?
   When will the world be generous
      to all instead of some?'

5. God asks, 'Who will go for me?
        Who will extend my reach?
    And who, when few will listen,
        will prophesy and preach?
    And who, when few bid welcome,
        will offer all they know?
    And who, when few dare follow,
        will walk the road I show?'

6. Amused in someone's kitchen,
        asleep in someone's boat,
    attuned to what the ancients
        exposed, proclaimed and wrote,
    a saviour without safety,
        a tradesman without tools
    has come to tip the balance
        with fishermen and fools.

John L. Bell and Graham Maule

[Verses marked * may be omitted.]

64

Iona Gloria

Gloria, gloria, gloria
in excelsis Deo.

Liturgical text

65

Jesu tawa pano;
Jesu tawa pano;
Jesu tawa pano;
tawa pano, mu zita renyu.

66

1. Jesus calls us here to meet him
as, through word and song and prayer,
we affirm God's promised presence
where his people live and care.
Praise the God who keeps his promise;
praise the Son who calls us friends;
praise the Spirit who, among us,
to our hopes and fears attends.

2. Jesus calls us to confess him
Word of Life and Lord of all,
sharer of our flesh and frailness
saving all who fail or fall.
Tell his holy human story;
tell his tales that all may hear;
tell the world that Christ in glory
came to earth to meet us here.

3. Jesus calls us to each other:
vastly different though we are;
race and colour, class and gender
neither limit nor debar.
Join the hand of friend and stranger;
join the hands of age and youth;
join the faithful and the doubter
in their common search for truth.

4. Jesus calls us to his table
rooted firm in time and space,
where the church in earth and heaven
finds a common meeting place.

Share the bread and wine, his body;
share the love of which we sing;
share the feast for saints and sinners
hosted by our Lord and King.

John L. Bell and Graham Maule

67

1. Jesus Christ is waiting,
   waiting in the streets;
   no one is his neighbour,
   all alone he eats.
   Listen, Lord Jesus,
   I am lonely too.
   Make me, friend or stranger,
   fit to wait on you.

2. Jesus Christ is raging,
   raging in the streets,
   where injustice spirals
   and real hope retreats.
   Listen, Lord Jesus,
   I am angry too.
   In the Kingdom's causes
   let me rage with you.

3. Jesus Christ is healing,
   healing in the streets;
   curing those who suffer,
   touching those he greets.
   Listen, Lord Jesus,
   I have pity too.
   Let my care be active,
   healing just like you.

4. Jesus Christ is dancing,
   dancing in the streets,

where each sign of hatred
he, with love, defeats.
Listen, Lord Jesus,
I should triumph too.
Where good conquers evil
let me dance with you.

5. Jesus Christ is calling,
   calling in the streets,
   'Who will join my journey?
   I will guide their feet'.
   Listen, Lord Jesus,
   let my fears be few.
   Walk one step before me;
   I will follow you.

John L. Bell and Graham Maule

68

Jubilate, everybody,
serve the Lord in all your ways,
and come before his presence singing,
enter now his courts with praise.
For the Lord our God is gracious,
and his mercy everlasting.
Jubilate, jubilate, jubilate Deo!

from Psalm 100(99),
paraphrased by Fred Dunn

69

Kyrie eleison.

Orthodox setting

70

Kyrie eleison

Lord, have mercy.
Lord, have mercy.
Christ, have mercy.
Christ, have mercy.
Lord, have mercy.
Lord, have mercy.

Liturgical text

71

1. Like the murmur of the dove's song,
   like the challenge of her flight,
   like the vigour of the wind's rush,
   like the new flame's eager might:
   come, Holy Spirit, come.

2. To the members of Christ's body,
   to the branches of the Vine,
   to the church in faith assembled,
   to her midst as gift and sign:
   come, Holy Spirit, come.

3. With the healing of division,
   with the ceaseless voice of prayer,
   with the power to love and witness,
   with the peace beyond compare:
   come, Holy Spirit, come.

Carl P. Daw Jr

72

1. Look and learn from the birds of the air,
   flying high above worry and fear;
   neither sowing nor harvesting seed,
   yet they're given whatever they need.
   If the God of earth and heaven
   cares for birds as much as this,
   won't he care much more for you,
   when you put your trust in him?

2. Look and learn from the flowers of the field,
   bringing beauty and colour to life;
   neither sewing nor tailoring cloth,
   yet they're dressed in the finest attire.
   If the God of earth and heaven
   cares for flowers as much as this,
   won't he care much more for you
   when you put your trust in him?

3. What God wants should be our will;
   where God calls should be our goal.
   When we seek the kingdom first,
   all we've lost is ours again.
   Let's be done with anxious thoughts,
   set aside tomorrow's cares,
   live each day that God provides
   putting all our trust in him.

Nah Young-Soo,
English version by John L. Bell

73

1. Look forward in faith –
   all time is in God's hand.
   Walk humbly with him
   and trust his future plan.
   God has wisely led
   his people by his power.
   Look forward in hope,
   he gives us each new hour.

2. Look forward in faith –
   the world is in God's care.
   His purpose of love
   he calls on us to share.
   In our neighbour's need
   the Lord is present still.
   He blesses the meek!
   The earth will know God's will.

3. Look forward in faith –
   God gives us life each day.
   Go onward with Christ,
   his Spirit guides our way.
   Now God lets us live
   within the sphere of grace.
   Trust ever in him –
   he rules o'er earth and space!

Andrew Scobie

74

1. Lord, for the years your love has kept and
   guided,
   urged and inspired us, cheered us on our way,

sought us and saved us, pardoned and
    provided:
Lord of the years, we bring our thanks today.

2.   Lord, for that Word, the Word of life which
      fires us,
    speaks to our hearts and sets our souls ablaze;
    teaches and trains, rebukes us and inspires us;
    Lord of the Word, receive your people's praise.

3.   Lord, for our land, in this our generation,
    spirits oppressed by pleasure, wealth and care;
    for young and old, for commonwealth and
      nation,
    Lord of our land, be pleased to hear our prayer.

4.   Lord, for our world; when we disown and
      doubt him,
    loveless in strength, and comfortless in pain,
    hungry and helpless, lost indeed without him;
    Lord of the world, we pray that Christ may
      reign.

5.   Lord for ourselves; in living power remake us –
    self on the cross and Christ upon the throne,
    past put behind us, for the future take us,
    Lord of our lives, to live for Christ alone.

Timothy Dudley-Smith

75

Lord Jesus Christ, lover of all,
trail wide the hem of your garment,
bring healing, bring peace.

John L. Bell and Graham Maule

76

1. Lord of life, we come to you;
   Lord of all, our Saviour be;
   come to bless and to heal
   with the light of your love.

2. Through the days of doubt and toil,
   in our joy and in our pain,
   guide our steps in your way,
   make us one in your love.

Catherine Walker

77

ANTIPHON:
   Lord, make me know your ways.

1. Lord, make me know your ways.
   Teach me your pathways, Lord.
   Teach me to walk in the truth of your ways.
   You are my Saviour, Lord.

2. Show me your mercy, Lord.
   In love remember me.
   Show me the love we have known from of old,
   now, in your goodness, Lord.

3. Yahweh is kind and true,
   guides those who go astray,
   shepherds the humble along the right path,
   teaches the poor his ways.

from Psalm 25(24),
Noel Donnelly

78

1. Lord, we come to ask your healing,
   teach us of love;
   all unspoken shame revealing,
   teach us of love.
   Take our selfish thoughts and actions,
   petty feuds, divisive factions,
   hear us now to you appealing,
   teach us of love.

2. Soothe away our pain and sorrow,
   hold us in love;
   grace we cannot buy or borrow,
   hold us in love.
   Though we see but dark and danger,
   though we spurn both friend and stranger,
   though we often dread tomorrow,
   hold us in love.

3. When the bread is raised and broken,
   fill us with love;
   words of consecration spoken,
   fill us with love.
   As our grateful prayers continue,
   make the faith that we have in you
   more than just an empty token,
   fill us with love.

4. Help us live for one another,
   bind us in love;
   stranger, neighbour, father, mother –
   bind us in love.
   All are equal at your table,
   through your Spirit make us able
   to embrace as sister, brother,
   bind us in love.

Jean Holloway

79

1. Lord, you have come to the lakeside
   looking neither for wealthy nor wise ones.
   You only asked me to follow humbly.

   *O Lord, with your eyes you have searched
      me,*
   kindly smiling, have spoken my name.
   *Now my boat's left on the shoreline behind
      me;*
   by your side I will seek other seas.

2. You know so well my possessions;
   my boat carries no gold and no weapons;
   but nets and fishes – my daily labour.

3. You need my hands, full of caring,
   through my labours to give others rest,
   and constant love that keeps on loving.

4. You, who have fished other oceans
   ever longed-for by souls who are waiting,
   my loving friend, as thus you call me.

ORIGINAL VERSE 1 AND REFRAIN:

1. Tú has venido^a la^orilla,
   no^has buscado ni^a sabios ni^a ricos,
   tan sólo quieres que yo te siga.

   Señor, me^has mirado a los ojos
   y sonriendo has dicho mi nombre.
   En la arena he dejado mi barca;
   junto^a ti buscaré otro mar.

Cesareo Gabarain,
translated by Robert Trupia

80

1. Love is the touch of intangible joy;
   love is the force that no fear can destroy;
   love is the goodness we gladly applaud:
   God is where love is, for love is of God.

2. Love is the lilt in a lingering voice;
   love is the hope that can make us rejoice;
   love is the cure for the frightened and flawed:
   God is where love is, for love is of God.

3. Love is the light in the tunnel of pain;
   love is the will to be whole once again;
   love is the trust of a friend on the road:
   God is where love is, for love is of God.

4. Love is the Maker and Spirit and Son;
   love is the kingdom their will has begun;
   love is the path which the saints all have trod:
   God is where love is, for love is of God.

Alison M. Robertson

81

1. Loving Spirit, loving Spirit,
   you have chosen me to be,
   you have drawn me to your wonder,
   you have set your sign on me.

2. Like a mother, you enfold me,
   hold my life within your own,
   feed me with your very body,
   form me of your flesh and bone.

3. Like a father, you protect me,
   teach me the discerning eye,
   hoist me up upon your shoulder,
   let me see the world from high.

4. Friend and lover, in your closeness
   I am known and held and blessed:
   in your promise is my comfort,
   in your presence I may rest.

5. Loving Spirit, loving Spirit,
   you have chosen me to be,
   you have drawn me to your wonder,
   you have set your sign on me.

Shirley Erena Murray

82
Mallaig Sprinkling Song

1. Spirit of God, come dwell within me.
   Open my heart, O come set me free,
   fill me with love for Jesus, my Lord,
   O fill me with living water.
   Jesus is living, Jesus is here.
   Jesus, my Lord, come closer to me.
   Jesus, our Saviour dying for me,
   and rising to save his people.

2. Lord, how I thirst, O Lord, I am weak.
   Lord, come to me, you alone do I seek.
   Lord, you are life, and love and hope,
   O fill me with living water.

3. Lord, I am blind, O Lord, I can't see.
   Stretch out your hand, O Lord, comfort me.

Lead me your way in light and in truth,
O fill me with living water.

Helen Kennedy

83

1. May the Lord, mighty God,
   bless and keep you forever;
   grant you peace, perfect peace,
   courage in every endeavour.

2. Lift up your eyes and see his face,
   and his grace for ever;
   may the Lord, mighty God,
   bless and keep you forever.

Blessing, from China

84

Mayenziwe 'ntando yakho.

Your will be done on earth, O Lord.

South African, from the Lord's Prayer

85

ANTIPHON:
*May your love be upon us, O Lord;
we place our trust in you.*

1. Oh the word of the Lord is faithful
   and the works of the Lord are true;

they speak of his love and his justice,
the face of the earth they renew.

2. The Lord looks on those who revere him,
   on the people who hope in his love.
   He will rescue their souls from damnation,
   from famine, from death, by his love.

3. Now my soul for its saviour is waiting
   for my Lord, my sword and my shield;
   may your love be upon us, your people,
   who place our trust in you.

from Psalm 33(32),
paraphrased by Michael Lloyd

86

1. Meekness and majesty, manhood and deity,
   in perfect harmony – the man who is God:
   Lord of eternity dwells in humanity,
   kneels in humility and washes our feet.
     Oh what a mystery – meekness and majesty:
     bow down and worship, for this is your God,
     this is your God!

2. Father's pure radiance, perfect in innocence,
   yet learns obedience to death on a cross:
   suffering to give us life, conquering through
       sacrifice –
   and, as they crucify, prays, 'Father forgive'.

3. Wisdom unsearchable, God the invisible,
   love indestructible in frailty appears:
   Lord of infinity, stooping so tenderly,
   lifts our humanity to the heights of his throne.

Graham Kendrick

87

Memorial Acclamation

When we eat this bread and drink this cup
we proclaim your death, Lord Jesus,
until you come in glory,
until you come in glory.

Liturgical text

88

1. Mothering God, you gave me birth
   in the bright morning of this world.
   Creator, Source of every breath,
   you are my rain, my wind, my sun;
   you are my rain, my wind, my sun.

2. Mothering Christ, you took my form,
   offering me your food of light,
   grain of life, and grape of love,
   your very body for my peace;
   your very body for my peace.

3. Mothering Spirit, nurturing one,
   in arms of patience hold me close,
   so that in faith I root and grow
   until I flower, until I know;
   until I flower, until I know.

Jean Janzen

89

SOLO: Night has fallen.
ALL: Night has fallen.
God our maker,
guard us sleeping.

Darkness now has come ...

We are with you, Lord ...

You have kept us, Lord ...

See your children, Lord ...

Keep us in your love ...

Now we go to rest ...

Malawian hymn,
adapted by Tom Colvin

90

PREPARATION: Now the silence,
now the peace,
now the empty hands uplifted.

CONFESSION: Now the kneeling,
now the plea,
ABSOLUTION: now the Father's arms in welcome.

SERMON: Now the hearing,
now the power,
OFFERTORY: now the vessel brimmed for
pouring.

COMMUNION:	Now the Body, now the Blood, now the joyful celebration.
UNION WITH CHRIST:	Now the wedding, now the songs, now the heart forgiven leaping.
CHANNELS OF GOD'S GRACE:	Now the Spirit's visitation, now the Son's epiphany, now the Father's blessing.

Now, now, now.

Jaroslav J. Vajda

91

Now go in peace,
now go in love,
from the Father above.
Jesus Christ the Son
stay with you till the day is done.
Holy Spirit encircle you
in all you think and do.
Once again God's blessing be with us.
Amen.

Michael Mair,
from Caribbean original

92

1. Now through the grace of God we claim
   this life to be his own,
   baptised with water in the name
   of Father, Spirit, Son.

2. For Jesus Christ the crucified,
   who broke the power of sin,
   now lives to plead for those baptised
   in unity with him.

3. So let us act upon his word,
   rejoicing in our faith,
   until we rise with Christ our Lord
   and triumph over death!

Michael Perry

93

1. O God, you are my God alone,
   whom eagerly I seek,
   though longing fills my soul with thirst
   and leaves my body weak.
   Just like a dry and barren land
   awaits a freshening shower
   I long within your house to see
   your glory and your power.

2. Your faithful love surpasses life,
   evoking all my praise.
   Through every day, to bless your name,
   my hands in joy I'll raise.
   My deepest needs you satisfy
   as with a sumptuous feast.
   So, on my lips and in my heart,
   your praise has never ceased.

3. Throughout the night I lie in bed
   and call you, Lord, to mind;
   in darkest hours I meditate
   how God, my strength, is kind.
   Beneath the shadow of your wing,
   I live and feel secure;

and daily as I follow close,
your right hand keeps me sure.

Psalm 63(62), paraphrased by John L. Bell

94

O Lord hear my prayer,
O Lord hear my prayer:
when I call answer me.
O Lord hear my prayer,
O Lord hear my prayer:
come and listen to me.

from Psalm 4, Taizé Community

95

1. O Lord, the clouds are gathering,
   the fire of judgement burns.
   How we have fallen!
   O Lord, you stand appalled to see
   your laws of love so scorned
   and lives so broken.

MEN:	*Have mercy, Lord,*
WOMEN:	*Have mercy, Lord,*
MEN:	*forgive us, Lord.*
WOMEN:	*forgive us, Lord.*
ALL:	*Restore us, Lord;*
	revive your church again.
MEN:	*Let justice flow*
WOMEN:	*Let justice flow*
MEN:	*like rivers,*
WOMEN:	*like rivers,*
ALL:	*and righteousness*
	like a never-failing stream.

2. Lord, over the nations now
   where is the dove of peace?
   Her wings are broken.
   O Lord, while precious children starve,
   the tools of war increase,
   their bread is stolen.

3. Lord, dark powers are poised to flood
   our streets with hate and fear.
   We must awaken!
   O Lord, let love reclaim the lives
   that sin would sweep away,
   and let your kingdom come!

4. Lord, your glorious cross shall tower
   triumphant in this land,
   evil confounding;
   through the fire, your suffering church display
   the glories of her Christ,
   praises resounding.

Graham Kendrick

96

INTRODUCTION:
   One day ... one day ...

REFRAIN:
   Oh the earth is the Lord's
   and all its weary people;
   oh the earth is the Lord's
   and everything that breathes.

   [sung twice]

1. One day (soon)
   there'll be fields for the poor;

one day (soon)
there'll be bread for us all.

2. One day (soon)
we will give up our riches,
walk in peace
with our brothers and sisters.

3. One day (soon)
we will learn to be righteous,
give back land
to the children of toil.

4. One day (soon)
we will bow down in sorrow,
leave our sin
and repent for tomorrow,
give back fields
and break up the plantations,
build a house
for the family of nations.

[The verse music is sung twice for verse 4]

CODA:
One day … one day …

Psalm 24(23),
adapted by Charles Irvine

97

1. Oh the life of the world is a joy and a treasure,
unfolding in beauty the green-growing tree,
the changing of seasons in mountain and valley,
the stars and the bright restless sea.

2. Oh the life of the world is a fountain of good-
       ness
    overflowing in labour and passion and pain,
    in the sound of the city and the silence of
       wisdom,
    in the birth of a child once again.

3. Oh the life of the world is the source of our
       healing.
    It rises in laughter and wells up in song;
    it springs from the care of the poor and the
       broken
    and refreshes where justice is strong.

4. So give thanks for the life and give love to the
       maker,
    and rejoice in the gift of the bright risen Son,
    and walk in the peace and the power of the
       Spirit
    till the days of our living are done.

Kathy Galloway

98

REFRAIN:
One bread, one body, one Lord of all,
one cup of blessing which we bless.
And we, though many, throughout the earth,
we are one body in this one Lord.

1. Gentile or Jew,
    servant or free,
    woman or man, no more.

2. Many the gifts,
    many the works,
    one in the Lord of all.

3. Grain for the fields,
   scattered and grown,
   gathered to one, for all.

John B. Foley

99

1. One is the body and one is the Head,
   one is the Spirit by whom we are led;
   one God and Father,
   one faith and one call for all.

2. Christ who ascended to heaven above
   is the same Jesus whose nature is love,
   who once descended
   to bring to this earth new birth.

3. Gifts have been given well suited to each;
   some to be prophets, to pastor or preach,
   some, through the Gospel,
   to challenge, convert and teach.

4. Called to his service are women and men
   so that his body might ever again
   witness through worship,
   through deed and through word
   to Christ our Lord.

Ephesians 4: 11-16,
paraphrased by John L. Bell

100

1. One more step along the world I go,
   one more step along the world I go.
   From the old things to the new
   keep me travelling along with you.

And it's from the old I travel to the new.
Keep me travelling along with you.

2. Round the corners of the world I turn,
   more and more about the world I learn.
   All the new things that I see
   you'll be looking at along with me.

3. As I travel through the bad and good
   keep me travelling the way I should.
   Where I see no way to go
   you'll be telling me the way, I know.

4. Give me courage when the world is rough,
   keep me loving though the world is tough.
   Leap and sing in all I do,
   keep me travelling along with you.

5. You are older than the world can be,
   you are younger than the life in me.
   Ever old and ever new,
   keep me travelling along with you.

Sydney Carter

101
Peruvian Gloria

CANTOR:	Glory to God, glory to God, glory in the highest!
ALL:	*Glory to God, glory to God, glory in the highest!*
CANTOR:	To God be glory forever!
ALL:	*To God be glory forever!*

| CANTOR: | Alleluia! Amen! |
| GROUP 1: | *Alleluia! Amen! ... |

[*Repeated until all three
groups are singing.]

Liturgical text

102

1. Praise God for the harvest of orchard and field,
   praise God for the people who gather their yield,
   the long hours of labour, the skills of a team,
   the patience of science, the power of machine.

2. Praise God for the harvest that comes from afar,
   from market and harbour, the sea and the shore:
   foods packed and transported, and gathered and
      grown
   by God-given neighbours, unseen and unknown.

3. Praise God for the harvest that's quarried and
      mined,
   then sifted, and smelted, or shaped and refined;
   for oil and for iron, for copper and coal,
   praise God, who in love has provided them all.

4. Praise God for the harvest of science and skill,
   the urge to discover, create and fulfil:
   for dreams and inventions that promise to gain
   a future more hopeful, a world more humane.

5. Praise God for the harvest of mercy and love
   for leaders and peoples who struggle and serve
   with patience and kindness, that all may be led
   to freedom and justice, and all may be fed.

Brian Wren

103

1. Put peace into each other's hands
    and like a treasure hold it,
  protect it like a candle-flame,
    with tenderness enfold it.

2. Put peace into each other's hands
    with loving expectation;
  be gentle in your words and ways,
    in touch with God's creation.

3. Put peace into each other's hands
    like bread we break for sharing;
  look people warmly in the eye:
    our life is meant for caring.

4. As at communion, shape your hands
    into a waiting cradle;
  the gift of Christ receive, revere,
    united round the table.

5. Put Christ into each other's hands,
    he is love's deepest measure;
  in love make peace, give peace a chance,
    and share it like a treasure.

Fred Kaan

104

1. Restore, O Lord, the honour of your name!
  In works of sovereign power
  come shake the earth again,
  that all may see, and come with reverent fear
  to the Living God,
  whose Kingdom shall outlast the years.

2. Restore, O Lord, in all the earth your fame,
   and in our time revive
   the Church that bears your name,
   and in your anger, Lord, remember mercy,
   O Living God,
   whose mercy shall outlast the years.

3. Bend us, O Lord, where we are hard and cold,
   in your refiner's fire;
   come purify the gold:
   though suffering comes, and evil crouches near,
   still our Living God
   is reigning, he is reigning here.

Graham Kendrick and Chris Rolinson

105

Sent by the Lord am I;
my hands are ready now
to make the earth the place
in which the kingdom comes.
Sent by the Lord am I;
my hands are ready now
to make the earth the place
in which the kingdom comes.

The angels cannot change
a world of hurt and pain
into a world of love,
of justice and of peace.
The task is mine to do,
to set it really free.
Oh, help me to obey;
help me to do your will.

Jorge Maldonado, from Chile

106

1. Safe in the shadow of the Lord
   beneath his hand and power,
   I trust in him,
   I trust in him,
   my fortress and my tower.

2. My hope is set on God alone
   though Satan spreads his snare,
   I trust in him,
   I trust in him,
   to keep me in his care.

3. From fears and phantoms of the night,
   from foes about my way,
   I trust in him,
   I trust in him,
   by darkness as by day.

4. His holy angels keep my feet
   secure from every stone;
   I trust in him,
   I trust in him,
   and unafraid go on.

5. Strong in the Everlasting Name,
   and in my Father's care,
   I trust in him,
   I trust in him,
   who hears and answers prayer.

6. Safe in the shadow of the Lord,
   possessed by love divine,
   I trust in him,
   I trust in him,
   and meet his love with mine.

from Psalm 91(90), Timothy Dudley-Smith

107

Sanctus and
Benedictus qui venit

Holy, holy, holy Lord.
God of power and might.
Heaven and earth are full of your glory.
Hosanna in the highest.

Blessed is he,
O blessed is he
who comes in the name of the Lord.
Hosanna in the highest.
Hosanna in the highest.

Liturgical text

108

1. Sing of the Lord's goodness, Father of all
     wisdom,
   come to him and bless his name.
   Mercy he has shown us, his love is for ever,
   faithful to the end of days.
   *Come then all you nations, sing of your
       Lord's goodness,*
   melodies of praise and thanks to God.
   *Ring out the Lord's glory, praise him with
       your music,*
   worship him and bless his name.

2. Power he has wielded, honour is his garment,
   risen from the snares of death.
   His word he has spoken, one bread he has
     broken,
   new life he now gives to all.

3. Courage in our darkness, comfort in our sorrow,
   Spirit of our God most high;
   solace for the weary, pardon for the sinner,
   splendour of the living God.

4. Praise him with your singing, praise him with
     the trumpet,
   praise God with the lute and harp;
   praise him with the cymbals, praise him with
     your dancing,
   praise God till the end of days.

Ernest Sands

109

1. She comes with mother's kindnesses
   and bends to touch and heal.
   She gives her heart away in love
   for those who cannot feel.

2. She comes with lover's tenderness
   to answer love's appeal.
   She gives her body with her heart
   to make her passion real.

3. She comes with worker's faithfulness
   to sow and reap and spin.
   She bends her back in common task
   to gather harvest in.

4. She comes with artist's joyfulness
   to make and shape and sing.
   She gives her hands and from them grows
   a free and lovely thing.

5. She comes, a child in humbleness
   and trust is in her eyes.
   And through them all of life appears
   in wondering surprise.

6. She comes with sister's carefulness
   strong to support and bind.
   Her voice will speak for justice' sake
   and peace is in her mind.

7. She comes with power like the night
   and glory like the day.
   Her reign is in the heart of things –
   Oh come to us and stay.

Kathy Galloway

110
Shine, Jesus, shine

1. Lord, the light of your love is shining,
   in the midst of the darkness, shining:
   Jesus, Light of the world, shine upon us;
   set us free by the truth you now bring us –
   shine on me, shine on me.

   Shine, Jesus, shine,
   fill this land with the Father's glory;
   blaze, Spirit, blaze,
   set our hearts on fire.
   Flow, river, flow,
   flood the nations with grace and mercy;
   send forth your word, Lord,
   and let there be light!

2. Lord, I come to your awesome presence,
   from the shadows into your radiance;
   by your blood I may enter your brightness:
   search me, try me, consume all my darkness,
   shine on me, shine on me.

3. As we gaze on your kingly brightness
   so our faces display your likeness,
   ever changing from glory to glory:
   mirrored here, may our lives tell your story.
   Shine on me, shine on me.

Graham Kendrick

111

1. Sing for God's glory
   that colours the dawn of creation,
   racing across the sky,
   trailing bright clouds of elation;
   sun of delight succeeds the velvet of night,
   warming the earth's exultation.

2. Sing for God's power
   that shatters the chains that would bind us,
   searing the darkness of
   fear and despair that could blind us,
   touching our shame with love that will not lay
       blame,
   reaching out gently to find us.

3. Sing for God's justice
   disturbing each easy illusion,
   tearing down tyrants
   and putting our pride to confusion;
   lifeblood of right, resisting evil and slight,
   offering freedom's transfusion.

4. Sing for God's saints who have
travelled faith's journey before us,
who in our weariness
give us their hope to restore us;
in them we see the new creation to be,
spirit of love made flesh for us.

Kathy Galloway

112

1. Sing to God with gladness, all creation,
sing to God the song of God's great love,
sing to God who made the heavens,
sing to God who made the loveliness of earth!
Sing to the Lord, sing Alleluia,
sing to the Lord, sing with joy!

2. Sing to God on high, O sun in splendour,
sing to God on high, O silver moon,
sing to God, O sky at dawning,
sing to God, O starlit silence of the night!

3. Sing your song of glory, angel voices,
sing your song of peace to all on earth,
sing of peace, the heart's deep longing,
sing of peace that comes from God and God
alone!

4. Sing to God the Father, all creation,
sing to God his dear and only Son,
sing to God the loving Spirit,
sing with joy to God, one God, for evermore!

James Quinn

113

1. Sing to the world of Christ our sovereign Lord,
   tell of his birth which brought new life to all.
   Speak of his life, his love, his holy word;
   let every nation hear and know his call.
   Sing to the world of Christ our sovereign Lord.

2. Sing to the world of Christ the Prince of Peace,
   showing to us the Father's loving care,
   pleading that love should reign and wars might
     cease,
   teaching we need the love of God to share.
   Sing to the world of Christ the Prince of Peace.

3. Sing to the world of Christ our steadfast friend,
   offering himself to live the constant sign,
   food for our souls until we meet life's end,
   gives us his flesh for bread, his blood for wine.
   Sing to the world of Christ our steadfast friend.

4. Sing to the world of Christ our Saviour King,
   born that his death that world's release should
     win.
   Hung on a cross, forgiveness he could bring;
   buried, he rose to conquer death and sin.
   Sing to the world of Christ our Saviour King.

5. Sing to the world of Christ at God's right hand,
   praise to the Spirit both have sent from heaven.
   Living in us till earth shall reach its span,
   time be no more, and Christ shall come again.
   Sing to the world of Christ at God's right hand.

Patrick Lee

114

REFRAIN: [sung twice]

Singing, we gladly worship the Lord together.
Singing, we gladly worship the Lord.
Those who are travelling the road of life
sow seeds of peace and love.

1. Come, bringing hope into a world of fear,
   a world which is burdened down with dread,
   a world which is yearning for a greater love
   but needs to be shown the true way.

2. Come bringing joyfully in both your hands
   some kindling to light the path to peace,
   some hope that there is a more human world
   where justice and truth will be born.

3. Whenever hatefulness and violence
   are banished for ever from our hearts,
   then will the world believe the day is near
   when sadness and pain shall find their end.

* * *

ORIGINAL REFRAIN:

Vienen con alegria, Señor,
cantando vienen con alegria, Señor,
los que camina por la vida, Señor
sembrando tu paz y amor.

Guatemalan traditional,
translated by Christine Carson

115

Some hae meat and canna eat,
and some wad eat that want it,
but we hae meat and we can eat;
sae let the Lord be thankit.

attributed to Robert Burns

116

Spirit of the living God, fall afresh on me,
Spirit of the living God, fall afresh on me:
break me, melt me, mould me, fill me.
Spirit of the living God, fall afresh on me.

Daniel Iverson

117

Spirit of God, unseen as the wind,
gentle as is the dove,
teach us the truth and help us believe,
show us the Saviour's love.

1. You spoke to us long, long ago,
    gave us the written word;
    we read it still, needing its truth,
    through it God's voice is heard.

    Spirit of God ...

2. Without your help we fail our Lord,
    we cannot live his way;

we need your power, we need your strength,
following Christ each day.

Spirit of God ...

Margaret Olds

118

CHORUS:
*Spirit of the Lord, Spirit of the Lord,
Spirit of the Lord, bear your fruit in me.*

Love, love, love, let there be love in me.

Joy ... let there be joy in me.

Patience ... let there be patience in me.

Kindness ... let there be kindness in me.

Goodness ... let there be goodness in me.

Faithfulness ... let there be faithfulness in me.

Gentleness ... let there be gentleness in me.

Self-control ... let there be self-control in me.

Ian White

119

1. Spirit of truth and grace,
   come to us in this place
   as now in Jesus' name God's people gather.

Open our eyes to see
truths that will ever be,
and in communion draw us close together.

2. Spirit of joy and peace,
   make all anxieties cease
   with knowledge of the Father's perfect caring.
   Then may God's children know
   love that won't let us go
   and joy that fills each day, beyond comparing.

3. Spirit of life and power,
   revive us in this hour
   and stir our hearts to praise with true devotion.
   Fill us with heavenly fire,
   and every heart inspire,
   that we may serve the world with your
   compassion.

Iain D. Cunningham

120

Stay with me, remain here with me.
Watch and pray, watch and pray.

Matthew 26: 28, 41, Taizé Community

121

The peace of the earth be with you,
the peace of the heavens too;
the peace of the rivers be with you,
the peace of the oceans too.
Deep peace falling over you.
God's peace growing in you.

Guatemalan, trans. Christine Carson

122

1. Take this moment, sign and space;
   take my friends around;
   here among us make the place
   where your love is found.

2. Take the time to call my name,
   take the time to mend
   who I am and what I've been,
   all I've failed to tend.

3. Take the tiredness of my days,
   take my past regret,
   letting your forgiveness touch
   all I can't forget.

4. Take the little child in me,
   scared of growing old;
   help *him/her* here to find *his/her* worth
   made in Christ's own mould.

5. Take my talents, take my skills,
   take what's yet to be;
   let my life be yours, and yet,
   let it still be me.

John L. Bell and Graham Maule

123

1. The God who sings
   a new world into being shows the way
   for many voices, varied gifts to sound
   in symphony.

2. The God who shouts
    in fury when the powerful shame the poor
    will break the chains, and those who hide in fear
    he will restore.

3. The God who weeps
    when fields lie barren and the missiles fall
    throws wide his arms and offers in his love
    refuge for all.

4. The God who laughs
    as unexpected overturns routine
    releases us to risk in faith, and find
    what joy can mean.

5. The God who calls
    in hearts of those who hear his Chosen One
    forgives, transforms, empowers, renews us while
    we journey on.

Douglas Galbraith

124

The Hand of Heaven

1. We who live by sound and symbol,
    we who learn from sight and word,
    find these married in the person
    of the one we call our Lord.
    Taking bread to be his body,
    taking wine to be his blood,
    he let thought take flesh in action,
    he let faith take root in food.

2. Not just once with special people,
    not just hidden deep in time,
    but wherever Christ is followed,

earthly fare becomes sublime.
Though to sound this be a mystery,
though to sense it seem absurd,
yet in faith, which seems like folly,
we meet Jesus Christ our Lord.

3. God, our Maker, send your Spirit,
consecrate the bread we break.
Let it bring the life we long for
and the love which we forsake.
Bind us closer to each other,
both forgiving and forgiven;
give us grace in this and all things
to discern the hand of heaven.

John L. Bell and Graham Maule

125

The Last Journey

1. From the falter of breath,
through the silence of death,
to the wonder that's breaking beyond;
God has woven a way,
unapparent by day,
for all those of whom heaven is fond.

2. From frustration and pain,
through hope hard to sustain,
to the wholeness here promised, there known;
Christ has gone where we fear
and has vowed to be near
on the journey we make on our own.

3. From the dimming of light,
through the darkness of night,

to the glory of goodness above;
God the Spirit is sent
to ensure heaven's intent
is embraced and completed in love.

4. From today till we die,
   through all questioning why,
   to the place from which time and tide flow;
   angels tread on our dreams
   and magnificent themes
   of heaven's promise are echoed below.

John L. Bell and Graham Maule

126

ANTIPHON:
The Lord is loving, the Lord is kind.

1. The Lord is kind, full of compassion,
   slow to anger, abounding in love.
   How good the Lord is to all,
   he shows compassion.
   The Lord is good to all his creatures.

2. The eyes of all creation look to you,
   and you give them the food that they need.
   All creatures thank you, O Lord,
   your friends shall bless you.
   The Lord is good to all his creatures.

3. The Lord is just in all his ways,
   he is loving in all his deeds.
   The Lord is close to all who call on him.
   The Lord is good to all his creatures.

from Psalm 145(144), Grail alt.

127

1. The Lord's my Shepherd, I'll not want.
   He makes me down to lie
   in pastures green: he leadeth me
   the quiet waters by.

2. My soul he doth restore again;
   and me to walk doth make
   within the paths of righteousness,
   even for his own Name's sake.

3. Yea, though I walk in death's dark vale,
   yet will I fear none ill:
   for thou art with me; and thy rod
   and staff me comfort still.

4. My table thou hast furnishèd
   in presence of my foes;
   my head thou dost with oil anoint,
   and my cup overflows.

5. Goodness and mercy all my life
   shall surely follow me:
   and in God's house for evermore
   my dwelling-place shall be.

Psalm 23(22), Scottish Psalter 1650

128

The Servant King

1. From heaven you came, helpless babe,
   entered our world, your glory veiled,
   not to be served but to serve,
   and give your life that we might live.

This is our God, the Servant King,
he calls us now to follow him,
to bring our lives as a daily offering
of worship to the Servant King.

2. There in the garden of tears
    my heavy load he chose to bear;
    his heart with sorrow was torn,
    'Yet not my will but yours,' he said.

3. Come see his hands and his feet,
    the scars that speak of sacrifice,
    hands that flung stars into space
    to cruel nails surrendered.

4. So let us learn how to serve
    and in our lives enthrone him,
    each other's needs to prefer,
    for it is Christ we're serving.

Graham Kendrick

129

LEADER: *Thuma mina.*
ALL: *Thuma mina, thuma mina,*
          thuma mina Somandla.

LEADER: Send me, Lord.
ALL: Send me, Jesus, send me, Jesus,
          send me, Jesus, send me, Lord.

          Lead me, Lord …

          Fill me, Lord …

          Thuma mina …

South African traditional hymn

130

1. There's a spirit in the air,
   telling Christians everywhere:
      'Praise the love that Christ revealed,
      living, working, in our world'.

2. Lose your shyness, find your tongue,
   tell the world what God has done:
      God in Christ has come to stay.
      Live tomorrow's life today!

3. When believers break the bread,
   when a hungry child is fed,
      praise the love that Christ revealed,
      living, working, in our world.

4. Still the Spirit gives us light,
   seeing wrong and setting right:
      God in Christ has come to stay.
      Live tomorrow's life today!

5. When a stranger's not alone,
   where the homeless find a home,
      praise the love that Christ revealed,
      living, working, in our world.

6. May the Spirit fill our praise,
   guide our thoughts and change our ways.
      God in Christ has come to stay.
      Live tomorrow's life today!

7. There's a Spirit in the air,
   calling people everywhere:
      'Praise the love that Christ revealed,
      living, working, in our world'.

Brian Wren

131

1. Through the love of God our Saviour
   all will be well.
   Free and changeless is his favour;
   all, all is well.
   Precious is the blood that healed us,
   perfect is the grace that sealed us,
   strong the hand stretched forth to shield us;
   all must be well.

2. Though we pass through tribulation,
   all will be well.
   Ours is such a full salvation,
   all, all is well.
   Happy still in God confiding,
   fruitful, if in Christ abiding,
   holy, through the Spirit's guiding;
   all must be well.

3. We expect a bright to-morrow;
   all will be well.
   Faith can sing through days of sorrow,
   'All, all is well.'
   On our Father's love relying,
   Jesus every need supplying,
   or in living or in dying,
   all must be well.

M. Peters

132

1. Till all the jails are empty
   and all the bellies filled;
   till no one hurts or steals or lies,
   and no more blood is spilled;

till age and race and gender
no longer separate;
till pulpit, press and politics
are free of greed and hate:
God has work for us to do.

2. In tenement and mansion,
in factory, farm, and mill,
in boardroom and in billiard-hall,
in wards where time stands still,
in classrooms, church, and office,
in shops or on the street;
in every place where people thrive
or starve or hide or meet:

3. By sitting at a bedside
to hold pale trembling hands,
by speaking for the powerless
against unjust demands,
by praying through our doing
and singing though we fear,
by trusting that the seed we sow
will bring God's harvest near:

Carl P. Daw Jr.

133

1. Today I awake
and God is before me.
At night, as I dreamt,
he summoned the day;
for God never sleeps
but patterns the morning
with slithers of gold
or glory in grey.

2. Today I arise
   and Christ is beside me.
   He walked through the dark
   to scatter new light.
   Yes, Christ is alive,
   and beckons his people
   to hope and to heal,
   resist and invite.

3. Today I affirm
   the Spirit within me
   at worship and work,
   in struggle and rest.
   The Spirit inspires
   all life which is changing
   from fearing to faith,
   from broken to blest.

4. Today I enjoy
   the Trinity round me,
   above and beneath,
   before and behind;
   the Maker, the Son,
   the Spirit together –
   they called me to life
   and call me their friend.

John L. Bell and Graham Maule

134

1. Touch the earth lightly,
   use the earth gently,
   nourish the life of the world in our care:
   gift of great wonder,
   ours to surrender,
   trust for the children tomorrow will bear.

2. We who endanger,
   who create hunger,
   agents of death for all creatures that live,
   we who would foster
   clouds of disaster,
   God of our planet, forestall and forgive!

3. Let there be greening,
   birth from the burning,
   water that blesses and air that is sweet,
   health in God's garden,
   hope in God's children,
   regeneration that peace will complete.

4. God of all living,
   God of all loving,
   God of the seedling, the snow and the sun,
   teach us, deflect us,
   Christ re-connect us,
   using us gently and making us one.

Shirley Erena Murray

135

To Christ the seed;
to Christ the sheaves:
so into God's barns
may we all be brought.

To Christ the sea;
to Christ the fish:
so into God's nets
may we all be caught.

From birth to growth,
from growth to age
may your two arms, O Christ,
fold us around.

From age to death,
from death to new birth
in the palace of grace
may we be found.

Irish traditional,
translated by J.W.

* * *

SECOND VERSION:

The seed is Christ's,
the harvest his:
may we be stored
within God's barn.

The sea is Christ's,
the fish are his:
may we be caught
within God's net.

From birth to age,
from age to death,
enfold us, Christ,
within your arms.

Until the end,
the great re-birth,
Christ, be our joy
in Paradise.

Irish traditional,
translated by James Quinn

136
Tree of Life

1. Tree of Life and awesome mystery,
   in your death we are reborn.
   Though you die in all of history,
   still you rise with every morn,
   still you rise with every morn.

2. Seed that dies to rise in glory,
   may we see ourselves in you.
   If we learn to live your story
   we may die to rise anew ...

3. We remember truth once spoken,
   love passed on through act and word.
   Every person lost and broken
   wears the body of our Lord ...

4. Gentle Jesus, mighty Spirit,
   come inflame our hearts anew.
   We may all your joy inherit
   if we bear the cross with you ...

5. Christ, you lead and we shall follow,
   stumbling though our steps may be.
   One with you in joy and sorrow,
   we the river, you the sea ...

Marty Haugen

137

1. Trim the cruisie's failing light;
   the Son of God shall pass tonight,
   shall pass at midnight dreary,
   the Son of Mary weary.

2. Lift the sneck and wooden bar
   and leave the stranger's door ajar
   lest he may tarry lowly,
   the Son of Mary holy.

3. Sweep the hearth and pile the peat
   and set the board with bread and meat;
   the Son of God may take it,
   the Son of Mary break it.

Rune of Barra,
translated by Murdoch MacLean

138

1. We cannot measure how you heal
   or answer every sufferer's prayer,
   yet we believe your grace responds
   where faith and doubt unite to care.
   Your hands, though bloodied on the cross,
   survive to hold and heal and warn,
   to carry all through death to life
   and cradle children yet unborn.

2. The pain that will not go away,
   the guilt that clings from things long past,
   the fear of what the future holds,
   are present as if meant to last.
   But present too is love which tends
   the hurt we never hoped to find,
   the private agonies inside,
   the memories that haunt the mind.

3. So some have come who need your help
   and some have come to make amends,
   as hands which shaped and saved the world
   are present in the touch of friends.
   Lord, let your Spirit meet us here

to mend the body, mind, and soul,
to disentangle peace from pain,
and make your broken people whole.

John L. Bell and Graham Maule

139

We are marching in the light of God.

Siyahamb' ekukhanyen' kwenkhos.

South African traditional

140
Well begun

1. Spirit of God, I long to live
   a life, not act a part.
   Confused and hurt, I ask you now
   to show me where to start.

2. Here, in the loneliness of pain,
   keep company with me.
   My body is your space. Make room
   for courage. Set me free.

3. Deep in the hidden heart of fear,
   my hope is turning sour.
   Prepare and help my anxious mind
   to open to your power.

4. Lost in a restless rush for change,
   my spirit lacks the pace.
   Express yourself in me. Present
   a challenge, not a race.

5. Spirit of God, be real in me,
   with me becoming one;
   make body, mind, and spirit whole,
   and I am well begun.

Alison M. Robertson

141

1. What shall we pray for those who died,
   those on whose death our lives relied?
   Silenced by war but not denied,
   God give them peace.

2. What shall we pray for those who mourn
   friendships and love, their fruit unborn?
   Though years have passed, hearts still are torn;
   God give them peace.

3. What shall we pray for those who live
   tied to the past they can't forgive,
   haunted by terrors they relive?
   God give them peace.

4. What shall we pray for those who know
   nothing of war, and cannot show
   grief or regret for friend or foe?
   God give them peace.

5. What shall we pray for those who fear
   war, in some guise, may reappear
   looking attractive and sincere?
   God give them peace.

6. God give us peace and, more than this,
   show us the path where justice is;
   and let us never be remiss
   working for peace that lasts.

Carnwadric Parish Church (Glasgow)
Worship Group

142

1. When, in our music, God is glorified,
   and adoration leaves no room for pride,
   it is as though the whole creation cried:
   Alleluia!

2. How often, making music, we have found
   a new dimension in the world of sound,
   as worship moved us to a more profound
   Alleluia!

3. So has the Church, in liturgy and song,
   in faith and love, through centuries of wrong,
   borne witness to the truth in every tongue:
   Alleluia!

4. And did not Jesus sing a psalm that night
   when utmost evil strove against the Light?
   Then let us sing, for whom he won the fight:
   Alleluia!

5. Let every instrument be tuned for praise!
   Let all rejoice who have a voice to raise!
   And may God give us faith to sing always:
   Alleluia!

Fred Pratt Green

143

1. We lay our broken world
   in sorrow at your feet,
   haunted by hunger, war and fear,
   oppressed by power and hate.

2. Here human life seems less
   than profit, might and pride,

though to unite us all in you
you lived and loved and died.

3. We bring our broken towns
   our neighbours hurt and bruised;
   you show us how old pain and wounds
   for new life can be used.

4. We bring our broken loves,
   friends parted, families torn;
   then in your life and death we see
   that love must be reborn.

5. We bring our broken selves,
   confused and closed and tired;
   then through your gift of healing grace
   new purpose is inspired.

6. O Spirit, on us breathe
   with life and strength anew;
   find in us love, and hope, and trust,
   and lift us up to you.

Anna Briggs

144

When Jesus wept, the falling tear
in mercy flowed beyond all bound.
When Jesus groaned, a trembling fear
seized all the guilty world around.

William Billings

145

1. When our confidence is shaken
   in beliefs we thought secure;

when the spirit in its sickness
seeks but cannot find a cure:
God is active in the tensions
of a faith not yet mature.

2. Solar systems, void of meaning,
freeze the spirit into stone;
always our researches lead us
to the ultimate unknown:
faith must die, or come full circle
to its source in God alone.

3. In the discipline of praying,
when it's hardest to believe;
in the drudgery of caring,
when it's not enough to grieve:
faith, maturing, learns acceptance
of the insights we receive.

4. God is love; and he redeems us
in the Christ we crucify:
this is God's eternal answer
to the world's eternal why;
may we in this faith maturing
be content to live and die.

Fred Pratt Green

146

1. Whoever lives beside the Lord,
sheltering in the Almighty's shade,
shall say, 'My God, in you I trust,
my safety, my defender.'

2. From unseen danger and disease
God will keep you safe and sure;

beneath his wings a place you'll find,
a refuge from all danger.

3. You will not dread what darkness brings –
   hidden danger, deadly plague;
   nor will you fear in daylight hours,
   the evil that surrounds you.

4. A thousand may die at your side,
   thousands more fall close at hand;
   but with God's truth for strength and shield,
   no threat will ever touch you.

5. God says, 'I'll save from every harm
   those who know and love my name.
   In trouble I will honour them,
   and show them my salvation.'

from Psalm 91(90), John L. Bell

147
Wisdom's Table

1. In her house there is a table,
   richly laid with bread and wine.
   All the foolish are invited;
   she calls to us, 'Come and dine'.
   > *Come and eat at Wisdom's table,*
   > *come and lay your burden down;*
   > *come and learn the power of weakness –*
   > *Wisdom's cross and Wisdom's crown.*

2. In this world we will have trouble
   and our comforters will fail;
   all our answers will seem useless,
   all our hopes will seem unreal.

3. There are roads which lead to danger,
   there are paths which lead to life:
   Wisdom's ways are filled with choices
   for the travellers she invites.

4. There are those who search for reasons,
   there are those who look for signs:
   Wisdom dances on the tombstone
   of the fool who bled and died.

Doug Gay

148

1. Will you come and follow me
   if I but call your name?
   Will you go where you don't know
   and never be the same?
   Will you let my love be shown,
   will you let my name be known,
   will you let my life be grown
   in you and you in me?

2. Will you leave your self behind
   if I but call your name?
   Will you care for cruel and kind
   and never be the same?
   Will you risk the hostile stare
   should your life attract or scare,
   will you let me answer prayer
   in you and you in me?

3. Will you let the blinded see
   if I but call your name?
   Will you set the prisoners free
   and never be the same?
   Will you kiss the leper clean

and do such as this unseen,
and admit to what I mean
in you and you in me?

4. Will you love the 'you' you hide
    if I but call your name?
    Will you quell the fear inside
    and never be the same?
    Will you use the faith you've found
    to reshape the world around
    through my sight and touch and sound
    in you and you in me?

5   Lord, your summons echoes true
    when you but call my name.
    Let me turn and follow you
    and never be the same.
    In your company I'll go
    where your love and footsteps show.
    Thus I'll move and live and grow
    in you and you in me.

John L. Bell and Graham Maule

149

You shall go out with joy
and be led forth with peace,
and the mountains and the hills
shall break forth before you.
There'll be shouts of joy
and the trees of the field shall clap,
shall clap their hands,
and the trees of the field shall clap their hands,
and the trees of the field shall clap their hands,
and the trees of the field shall clap their hands
and you'll go out with joy.

Stuart Dauermann

150

You show your friends the path of life,
give them the fullness of joy.

1. I say to the Lord: you are my God.
    Happiness lies in you alone.
    He put in my heart a marvellous love,
    love for the faithful who dwell in his land.

2. O Lord it is you, my portion and my cup,
    you yourself who are my prize.
    I bless the Lord who counsels me,
    even at night he directs my heart.

3. My heart and soul rejoice and are glad,
    even my body shall safely rest.
    You will not leave my soul with the dead,
    nor let your beloved know decay.

Psalm 16(15), Grail alt.

List

✳

OF COPYRIGHT HOLDERS
AND ADMINISTRATORS

For a song to be reproduced for local use (*eg* in a service sheet or on overhead transparency), permission must be sought from the copyright holders or administrators. This is not obtained from the publisher of the book, but from the owners of each individual hymn. These are:

1	WGRG Iona Community
2	Calamus
4	Calamus
8	Calamus
9	Stainer & Bell Ltd
10	Calamus
11	WGRG Iona Community
12	Kingsway's Thankyou Music
15	Calamus
16	Kingsway's Thankyou Music
17	WGRG Iona Community
18	World Council of Churches
19	Calamus
20	WGRG Iona Community
21	Calamus
22	CopyCare Ltd
23	Panel on Worship
25	Panel on Worship
26	Noel Donnelly
27	Jubilate Hymns Ltd
28	Panel on Worship
29	Michael Mair
30	Calamus
31	Calamus
32	WGRG Iona Community
33	ICEL Inc.
34	Stainer & Bell Ltd
35	Panel on Worship
36	Stainer & Bell Ltd
37	Kevin Mayhew Ltd
38	Calamus
39	WGRG Iona Community
40	WGRG Iona Community
41	Iain D. Cunningham
42	WGRG Iona Community
43	CopyCare Ltd
44	Panel on Worship

Addresses

✳

OF COPYRIGHT HOLDERS
AND ADMINISTRATORS

A. P. Watt Ltd: 20 John Street, LONDON WC1N 2DR
 (Tel: 0171 405 6774; Fax: 0171 831 2154)
Abingdon Press (*see* United Nations Music Publishing Ltd)
Ateliers et Presses de Taizé (*see* Calamus)
Bandleader Publications: 7 Garrick Street, LONDON WC2E 9AR
Baptist Union of Great Britain and Ireland: P.O. Box 44,
 129 Broadway, DIDCOT OX11 8RT (Tel: 01235 512077)
Boosey & Hawkes Ltd: The Hyde, Edgeware Road, LONDON NW9
 6JN (Tel: 0181 205 3861; Fax: 0181 205 8530)
Broomhill Church of Scotland: c/o The Manse, 27 St Kilda Drive,
 GLASGOW G14 9LN (Tel: 0141 959 3204)
Calamus: 30 North Terrace, MILDENHALL IP28 7AB
 (Tel: 01638 716579; Fax: 01638 510390)
Carnwadric Parish Church (Glasgow) Worship Group
 (*contact* WGRG Iona Community)
Cassell (Publishers) plc: Villiers House, Strand, LONDON WC2N
 5JE (Tel: 0171 839 4900)
Common Ground Editors: (*contact* Panel on Worship)
CopyCare Ltd: P.O. Box 77, HAILSHAM BN27 3EF
 (Tel: 01323 840942; Fax: 01323 849355)
Copyright control (*contact* Panel on Worship)
Cunningham, Rev. Iain D: 9 Station Road, CARLUKE ML8 5AA
 (Tel/Fax: 01555 771262)
Dellow, Ronald: 8 Lynch Street, Point Chevalier, AUCKLAND 2,
 Aotearoa New Zealand
Donnelly, Dr Noel S: 80 Cardross Road, DUMBARTON G82 4JQ
 (Tel: 01389 600886)
Dudley-Smith, Rt. Rev. Timothy: 9 Ashlands, Ford, SALISBURY SP4
 6DY (Tel: 01722 326417)
Ferguson, Colin (*contact* Panel on Worship)
Galloway, Rev. Ian: 44 Riverside Road, GLASGOW G43 2EF
 (Tel: 0141 649 5250)
Galloway, Rev. Kathy: 20 Hamilton Park Avenue, GLASGOW G12
 8DU (Tel: 0141 357 4079)
Gay, Rev. Doug: 16 Powerscroft Road, LONDON E5 0PU
 (Tel: 0181 985 2563)
Geoffrey Chapman (*see* Cassell [Publishers] plc)
GIA Publications Inc. (*see* Calamus)
Hope Publishing Co. (*see* CopyCare Ltd)
ICEL Inc. [International Commission on English in the Liturgy]:
 1522 K. Street NW, Suite 1000, Washington DC 20005, USA
 (Tel: 001 202 347 0800; Fax: 001 202 347 1839)
Jackson, Francis: Nether Garth, Acklam, MOULTON YR7 9RG

Janzen, Jean: 5508 E. Lane, Fresno, CALIFORNIA 93727, USA

Jubilate Hymns Ltd: 13 Stoddart Avenue, SOUTHAMPTON SO19 4ED (Tel: 01703 441884; Fax: 01703 442323)

Kevin Mayhew Ltd: Rattlesden, BURY ST EDMUNDS IP30 0SZ (Tel: 01449 737978; Fax: 01449 737834)

Kingsway's Thankyou Music: Lottbridge Drove, EASTBOURNE BN23 6NT (Tel: 01323 410930; Fax: 01323 411970)

Little Misty Music: P.O. Box 8, PERTH PH2 7EX

Lloyd, Michael: 22 Orchard Close, Rushwick, WORCESTER WR2 5TH

MacGorain, Riobard: Gael-Linn, 26 Merrion Square, DUBLIN 2

MacLean, Murdoch (*contact* Panel on Worship)

Mair, Rev. Michael: 31 Cranford Road, ABERDEEN AB10 7NJ (Tel: 01224 318527)

Make Way Music: P.O. Box 263, CROYDON CR9 5AP (Tel: 0181 656 0025)

Matsikenyiri, Patrick (*contact* Panel on Worship)

Mitchell, David: 99 St Leonard's Street (2F4), EDINBURGH EH8 9QY

OCP Publications (*see* Calamus)

Oxford University Press: Hymn Copyright, 70 Baker Street, LONDON W1M 1DJ (Tel: 0171 616 5900; Fax: 0171 616 5901)

Panel on Worship: Church of Scotland, 121 George Street, EDINBURGH EH2 4YN (Tel: 0131 225 5722; Fax: 0131 220 3113)

Peachey, Janet (*contact* Panel on Worship)

Peters, M. (*contact* Panel on Worship)

Public domain (*works so designated are free of copyright control*)

Robertson, Alison M: Manse of Canongate, EDINBURGH EH8 8BR (Tel/Fax: 0131 556 3515)

Röntgen, Johanna: Mankestraat 3, 2597 CJ THE HAGUE, Netherlands

St Mungo Music: Presbytery of St Leo the Great, 5 Beech Avenue, GLASGOW G41 5BY (Tel: 0141 427 0293)

School of Scottish Studies: 27 George Square, EDINBURGH EH8 9LD (Tel: 0131 650 4167)

Scobie, Rev. Andrew: The Manse, Cardross, DUMBARTON G82 5LB (Tel/Fax: 01389 841322)

Scripture Union: 207-209 Queensway, Bletchley, MILTON KEYNES MK2 2EB (Tel: 01908 856000; Fax: 01908 856111)

Stainer & Bell Ltd: P.O. Box 110, Victoria House, Gruneisen Road, LONDON N3 1DZ (Tel: 0181 343 3303; Fax: 0181 343 3024)

Steele, Andrea A: Kaimes, Main Road, Cardross, DUMBARTON G82 5PX (Tel: 01389 841818)

Sticky Music: 1 Ventnor Place, EDINBURGH EH9 2BP (Tel: 0131 667 2370)

The Sparrow Corporation (*see* CopyCare Ltd)

United Nations Music Publishing Ltd: 75 High Street, Needham Market, IPSWICH IP6 8AN

Wessmans Musikförlag (*see* Wild Goose Publications)

WGRG Iona Community (Wild Goose Resource Group): Pearce Institute, 840 Govan Road, GLASGOW G51 3UU (Tel 0141 445 4561; Fax: 0141 445 4295)

Wild Goose Publications: Unit 15, 6 Harmony Row, GLASGOW G51 3BA (Tel: 0141 440 0985; Fax: 0141 440 2338)

World Council of Churches: 150 route de Ferney, P.O. Box 2100, 1211 GENEVA 2, Switzerland (Tel: 0041 22 791 6111; Fax: 0041 22 791 0361)

Index

*

TITLES AND FIRST LINES
(TITLES IN ITALICS)